50 STORIES FOR SPECIAL OCCASIONS

D0625502

By the same author:
The Brownie Guide Handbook
Love Breaks Through
Jessica Joins the Brownies
Tracy and the Warriors
A Friend for Life
Failure Is Not Final
50 Five-Minute Stories

50 Stories for
Special Occasions

LYNDA NEILANDS

EASTBOURNE

Copyright © Lynda Neilands 1998

Illustrations copyright © Gillian Cooke

The right of Lynda Neilands to be identified
as author of this work has been asserted by her
in accordance with the Copyright, Designs
and Patents Act 1988.

First published 1998
Reprinted 1999, 2000

All rights reserved.
No part of this publication may be reproduced or
transmitted in any form or by any means, electronic
or mechanical, including photocopy, recording or any
information storage and retrieval system, without
permission in writing from the publisher.

ISBN 0 85476 749 5

Published by
KINGSWAY PUBLICATIONS
Lottbridge Drove, Eastbourne, BN23 6NT, England.
Email: books@kingsway.co.uk

Designed and produced for the publishers by
Bookprint Creative Services, P.O. Box 827, BN21 3YJ, England.
Printed in Great Britain.

For Hannah Ruth

Contents

APRIL: *The Easter Story*

MAY: *Party-Time*

JUNE: *Before and After*

JULY: *Winners and Losers*

AUGUST: *The Great Escape*
(*A Five-Part Serial Story*)

Acknowledgements

Many friends and acquaintances provided inspiration and information for the stories in this book. I am grateful to Paul Callaghan for 'Blaze and Dasher', to Denise and Davy Lappin for 'Romeo and Juliet', to Jenny Lewis for 'Mystery Tour', to Katie MacKinnon for 'Like Father, Like Son', to the Revd Nigel Mackey for 'The Monster', to Joy Molyneux for 'Talcum Powder and Safety Pins', to Ivor Poobalan and the Revd Dr Norman Taggart for 'Message of Hope', to Julie P. Warren for 'Lost and Found', to Brian Waltham for 'Catchem' and to Ruth Wilson for 'Out of the Cupboard'.

As ever my husband, David, has been a rock of support. I particularly appreciate the good grace with which he relinquished his computer when mine gave up the ghost!

Introduction

This is a book of stories for telling to children. Some are true stories. Some are made-up stories. A few are Bible stories. All, however, contain biblical truth. Some are more suited to lower primary school children. Others are geared towards the upper end of the scale. Many are 'all age' stories, designed to be understood at different levels by all ages (adults included). With each story a rough indication of the comprehension level has been included to help leaders select the most appropriate material for their group.

The book has been compiled with the needs of those looking for occasional and seasonable material particularly in mind. The stories are gathered under monthly headings – each cluster having its own seasonable theme and feel. Speakers will also find stories suitable for special occasions such as Valentine's Day, Father's Day and Bible Sunday included each month. Those looking for stories to illustrate particular subjects or Bible passages should turn to the subject and Scripture indexes at the back.

At the heart of the book is a five-part serial which can be used at any time of the year. 'The Great Escape' chronicles the imaginary adventures of four friends as they say goodbye to slavery in Egypt and set out for the Promised

Land. It is for use with upper primary children who regularly attend a Christian club or church-based group, and is designed to encourage them to own their faith.

Appended to each story are a teaching point, a Bible reading, a list of songs (from *Songs of Fellowship for Kids* and *Junior Praise*) and a story application. The application suggests one possible way in which the story-teller may create a bridge from the narrative to the Bible teaching point and make that point without losing the listeners' attention. At the younger end of the age range these suggestions include simple action rhymes and choruses; at the older end they include questions and symbols. It goes without saying that story-tellers should feel free to come up with their own applications. They should also feel free to abandon the application completely, letting the story drop like a pebble in a pond and create its own ripples.

Those ripples can be far-reaching. Good stories, among other things, teach values, touch the emotions, foster empathy, lodge in the memory and can be a powerful vehicle for spiritual truth. In short, time invested in story-telling is time well spent. Here then are a few tips for those wishing to develop their skills.

- Don't bury your head in a book or a script. Eye contact commands attention and adds life to what you say.
- Do involve the children in the story as appropriate, i.e. through questions, sound effects, repeating phrases, etc.
- Do aim to be visual. Gestures, facial expressions and a few clear illustrations will help bring the story to life.
- Do be expressive: changing pace, building excitement, using different voices for different characters. (If you do this, you may omit phrases like 'said so-and-so' or 'they gasped' from the narrative.)
- Do pay particular attention to the beginning and ending.

- Do practise your story.
- Don't go on for too long.

Happy story-telling!

JANUARY

Discoveries

1. *Three Cheers for Grady*

(New Year)

It was New Year's Eve. Outside Morely's Pet Shop the street was full of shoppers, and inside two children were inspecting the pets. They spent a long time looking at the fish tanks. 'Those fish are as bright as jewels,' the boy said.

Then they looked at some baby rabbits. 'Ah! Aren't they sweet!' the girl cooed.

Then they listened to the canaries. 'I wish I could sing like that!' the girl smiled.

Finally the pair had a word with the grey parrot at the back of the shop. 'Hi, Grady. What have you to say for yourself?'

'Hands up! Hands up!' the parrot squawked.

'She always says the same thing!' the boy laughed. 'Go on, Grady. Say something different. Say, "Hallo, kids!"'

16

'Ha-Ha-Hands up!' Grady squawked again.

The girl looked disappointed.

'Mr Morely should get himself another parrot,' shrugged her brother. 'That one will never say anything new.'

Outside the pet shop daylight was fading, and inside Mr Morely was getting ready to go home. 'It's New Year's Day tomorrow,' he told the pets. 'The shop will be shut, but I'll come in to feed you at the usual time.'

'Hands up!' cried Grady sadly. What she really meant was 'goodbye'. She'd spent the afternoon thinking about what the children had said, and she'd made up her mind. It was time for her to retire from the pet shop. She had decided to fly away.

Outside the pet shop darkness had fallen, and inside, speaking in bird language, Grady told the pets of her plans. 'I'll make my escape first thing tomorrow,' she told them. 'As soon as Mr Morely opens the door.'

'But where will you go?' sniffed a hamster.

'I'll go to a place where grey parrots eat grapes all day long,' said Grady. 'And where they don't have to talk to customers.'

'The children will miss you,' said the hamster.

'No they won't,' Grady shook her head. 'The children want to see fish and rabbits and canaries. They'll never miss an old grey parrot like me.'

Outside the pet shop the clocks struck twelve, and inside Grady tucked her head under her wing. Before long she was dreaming. It was a nice dream to begin with, but suddenly it turned chilly, as if she'd escaped from the pet shop and ended up at the North Pole.

'Brrrrr . . .' she shivered and opened her eyes, only to discover cold air streaming in from outside. The shop door was wide open.

For a moment this seemed lucky. She could leave straight away.

And then she spotted the intruders. Two masked men with torches were sneaking through the shop.

'Eeeek . . . eeek . . .' shrieked the terrified creatures, as the thieves started breaking into their cages and stuffing them into sacks.

Grady was the only one to keep calm. 'Hands up! Hands up!' she squawked at the top of her voice.

The thieves stopped in their tracks.

'It's the police,' they gasped. 'Run for it!'

Then they turned on their heels and shot out through the door, dropping their sacks as they went.

Outside the pet shop the world was celebrating, and inside the pets were celebrating too – squeaking, shrieking, cheeping, squealing. They made such a racket that the neighbours got worried and told Mr Morely to go and check out the shop.

What a sight met his eyes! He saw a row of empty cages and dozens of creatures romping round the floor. 'Three cheers for the pet whose words saved our skins! Hip hip hurrah!' they cried.

They were cheering for Grady; Grady, the parrot, who'd just discovered her words could have a big effect. 'Hands up! Hands up!' she was squawking with joy.

'My own dear Grady!' Mr Morely smiled.

And Grady felt so thankful, she came out with something quite amazing. 'Ha-Ha-Happy New Year,' she squawked.

Teaching point

God wants us to speak helpful words, not harmful words.

Bible reading

Ephesians 4:29.

Application

After telling the story, remind the group that Grady discovered her words had a big effect. Then say that our words can have a big effect too. Point out that sometimes the words which have the biggest effect can be small ones – words like 'thank you' and 'well done'. Ask what sort of effect these words have. Then ask if the group can think of a few words that can have the opposite effect, e.g. 'Go away! You're stupid!' Read Ephesians 4:29 and say that the Bible teaches we should try to use the first kind of words and try not to use the second. Encourage them to make this their New Year resolution and to ask God to help them keep it.

Songs

If I were a butterfly (SOFK 74, JP 94)
In our work and in our play (JP 108)
I want to walk with Jesus Christ (SOFK 100, JP 124)
Keep me shining, Lord (JP 147)
This little light of mine (JP 258)
Be holy in all that you do (JP 314)
It's not very nice saying 'Na na na na na na' (JP 401)
It's the little things that show our love for Jesus (JP 403)
Maybe you can't draw or sing or be a football star (JP 429)

2. The Wall

Once upon a time there was a wall.

A big, high wall.

A wide, hollow wall.

An ugly, wobbly wall.

It had been built between two bungalows by two men who didn't know much about building, Mr Chalk and Mr Cheese. They'd built it – red bricks on one side and grey bricks on the other – because they hated being neighbours. And they hated being neighbours because they were completely different.

Mr Chalk was a retired teacher – a book-lover, who enjoyed playing the violin and doing crosswords. Mr Cheese was a retired chef – a fun-lover, who enjoyed trying new recipes and throwing parties.

'Him and his noisy friends. They keep me awake until midnight,' Mr Chalk would moan.

'Him and his pesky violin. He wakes me up at six in the morning,' Mr Cheese would groan.

The only thing these gentlemen shared was a love of cats. Since moving in, Mr Chalk had taken up with a cat called Wordsworth, and Mr Cheese had been taken over by a cat called Kippers. Wordsworth slept most of the time and ate very little, while Kippers pounced on shadows, swung on the curtains and ate everything in sight. In other words, they seemed as different as their owners.

And then one day both cats went missing.

Mr Chalk realised that Wordsworth had gone first thing in the morning, when the animal wasn't curled up in his usual spot. Mr Cheese realised that Kippers had gone later in the day, when the cat didn't appear for lunch.

That afternoon both men headed off in different directions into the countryside to search for their pets.

'Wordy . . . Wordy . . . Wordy . . . Wordsworth,' called Mr Chalk.

'Kippy . . . Kippy . . . Kippy . . . Kippers,' called Mr Cheese.

But it was no good. After a whole afternoon of calling and searching, both men came home empty-handed.

For once they actually spoke to each other.

'Did you see a quiet, sensible cat called Wordsworth while you were out?' asked Mr Chalk.

'No,' said Mr Cheese. 'Did you see a noisy, crazy cat called Kippers?'

'No,' growled Mr Chalk. 'And I hope your naughty pet hasn't led mine into mischief.'

'Not a chance of it,' huffed Mr Cheese. 'Your Wordsworth is sad and boring. My Kippers wouldn't have anything to do with him.'

'How dare you!' shouted Mr Chalk. 'My Wordsworth is

extremely well bred – not at all the sort of cat to mix with
your Kippers.'

Just as things were turning nasty, a desperate mewing
filled the air. 'Miaow. . . miaow . . . miaow . . . miaow. . . .'

The two men spun round. To their surprise the sound
seemed to be coming from inside the wall. 'Miaow . . . miaow
. . . miaow. . . .'

Mr Chalk fetched a ladder. He climbed up and examined
the wall. Oh dear! He found a broad gap in the stonework.

'There's a hole,' he shouted down to Mr Cheese. 'Our cats
must have fallen through.'

Even as he spoke, the cats stopped mewing and started to
thump about.

'They're panicking,' cried Mr Chalk.

'Or fighting,' said Mr Cheese.

The thumping got worse. In fact it sounded as if *elephants*,
not cats, were hurling their bodies against the wall. Before
long cracks had appeared. Mr Chalk hurried down the
ladder. No sooner had he reached the ground than . . .
rumble . . . rumble . . . CRASH! The wall collapsed.

As the dust settled, a single marmalade cat stepped out
from the rubble, safe and sound.

'It's Wordsworth!' cried Mr Chalk.

'No it's not. It's Kippers!' cried Mr Cheese.

'Wordsworth,' repeated Mr Chalk.

'Kippers,' insisted Mr Cheese.

The cat rubbed round their ankles. And the penny
dropped. Kippers and Wordsworth were the same cat.

Shaking their heads in amazement, the cat's joint owners sat
down side by side on the ruins to work out how they'd
managed to share the same pet for so long without knowing it.

'No wonder he wasn't hungry when he came to me in the
mornings,' marvelled Mr Chalk.

'No wonder he was ready to eat and play when he came to
me in the afternoons,' grinned Mr Cheese.

They talked on, and Mr Cheese didn't find Mr Chalk boring, while Mr Chalk was delighted to discover how much Mr Cheese knew. At their feet a purring Kippers-Wordsworth washed his whiskers. It had been hard work bringing that wall down. But he was now one very happy cat.

Teaching point

God's love brings us together.

Bible reading

Ephesians 4:1–6.

Telling this story

Split the group into two. One half is to 'mew' quietly every time the name 'Wordsworth' is mentioned. The other half is to 'mew' loudly each time they hear the name 'Kippers'.

Application

Remind the group that in the story they have just heard Mr Chalk and Mr Cheese make an important discovery. They discovered that even though they were different, they shared the same pet. Get the children to tell you some of the obvious differences within your church or group (boys/girls, young/old, tall/small, etc.). Point out that even though we are different there are some things we all share. Say you are going to show them one very important thing we share. Can they work out what it is? Silently sign the first part of the action rhyme 'God loves me, God loves you' (see below). When the group have said what this means, explain how discovering God loves 'me' as much as 'you' should help us to love one another. Finish by teaching and repeating the whole rhyme.

God loves me,   (*point up, cross hands on chest, point to self*)
God loves you,   (*point up, cross hands on chest, point to others*)
God wants us to love each other too.   (*shake hands with partner*)

Songs

Bind us together, Lord (SOFK 10, JP 17)
He brought me to His banqueting house (JP 73)
I will sing, I will sing a song unto the Lord (SOFK 104,
    JP 126)
Jesus died for all the children (JP 132)
Put your hand in the hand of the man who stilled the water
    (JP 206)
We really want to thank You, Lord (SOFK 179, JP 268)
God loves you, and I love you (SOFK 42, JP 348)
I am the Church (JP 367)
Jerusalem man, walking from His homeland (JP 405)

3. *The Monster*

(A true story for World Leprosy Day)

Krishna lived high up in the mountains of Nepal. Hard but happy – that was the way she would have described the first seven years of her life. Hard, because she was one of a family of fourteen and poor harvests sometimes meant they didn't have much food. Happy, because it was fun to gather wood with her sisters and to help her mother with the cooking. Yes, for the first seven years of her life Krishna had a happy smile on her face. And then, with cruel suddenness, everything changed.

The girl was washing at a basin when she noticed the strange white patch on her smooth golden skin. She showed it to her mother, who cried out with fear: 'Leprosy. You've got leprosy.'

25

Next thing Krishna knew, she was living alone in an outside shed. Her family had been so afraid of catching leprosy, they'd driven her from the house. Leprosy, of course, is a disease which has been around for thousands of years. But to Krishna it was a monster – a monster who had turned everyone against her.

Time passed and the monster continued to ruin Krishna's life. It brought her face out in lumps and ate at her nose. It made her lose feeling in her hands and feet. With no pain to warn her that she was sitting too near the fire, or that a sharp stone was piercing her foot, she was soon covered in cuts and burns and bruises. Her family were sorry, but what could they do? They were afraid that if they touched Krishna the monster would get them too.

Then early one morning the little girl woke up to hear someone calling her name. 'Krishna! Krishna!' Slowly she dragged herself out of the dark shed into the open air, and there stood her father, all dressed for a journey, with a wicker basket on his back.

'Come.' He turned and started walking.

Puzzled, the girl followed him – out of the farm, through the village and down the mountain track. 'Where are we going?' she panted.

'Anandaban,' her father replied. The word meant 'Forest of Peace', which only left Krishna more puzzled than ever.

The wet monsoon was over and warm rays of sunlight were beginning to chase the mist from the mountain-tops. She saw plenty of mud-and-wattle houses, plenty of rocks and paddy fields, but no forest. . . .

By afternoon the girl's feet were bleeding and her father had to keep stopping to give her a chance to catch up. On and on they walked, until at last Krishna stumbled round a bend in the road and there, stretched out before them, was a long low building.

'That's Anandaban,' said her father.

'B-but . . . where are the trees?' Krishna gasped.

Her father set down his load. 'Anandaban is a hospital, not a forest,' he said quietly. 'The village leaders said I should bring you here.'

Krishna trembled and longed to hide. She wanted to be back in her shed, tucked out of sight, not meeting with strangers who would turn away from her like everyone else.

But when her father brought her into the building she made a discovery. People were different at Anandaban. Later she understood that they were Christians – followers of the God who had healed people who suffered from leprosy when he was on earth. To begin with, though, what really amazed her was that they weren't afraid to come close and touch her with their hands.

'Leprosy is really quite difficult to catch,' a kind nurse in a white sari explained as she rubbed ointment on Krishna's cuts. 'What's more, we can cure it. You will stay here for six months and take a tablet every day. Then you'll be ready to go back to your village. And don't worry, we'll see to it that everyone knows being near you is perfectly safe.'

And that was exactly what happened. Six months after Krishna arrived at Anandaban, her father collected her from the hospital. She travelled with him back up the mountain to the village where her mother, brothers and sisters were waiting to welcome her home. 'Come in! Come in!' they pulled her over to the fire.

Krishna sat down, almost crying with happiness. Here she was, back at the centre of her family, thanks to the people at Anandaban and to the God who'd helped them chase the monster from her life.

Teaching point

Jesus healed people with leprosy when he was on earth.

Bible reading

Mark 1:40–42.

Application

Before telling the story, arrange for the children to make handprints on a large sheet of paper. After telling it, hold up this sheet. Point out that although the hands are different sizes, each one is perfectly shaped – as we would expect among children living in this part of the world, where leprosy does not damage our bodies. (It is important to make this clear to younger children who could be afraid of catching the disease.) Then say that there is a story in the Bible about Jesus healing someone with leprosy, and read Mark 1:40–42. Ask whether the group can think how Jesus continues to heal sufferers from leprosy today (through caring doctors and nurses). Refer back to the handprints. In Anandaban, and in many other places, doctors and nurses use their hands as they bring healing. Finish by praying for their work.

Songs

Come to Jesus, 'He's amazing' (JP 33)

Father I place into Your hands (SOFK 28, JP 42)

If you see someone lying in the road (JP 95)

Jesus' hands were kind hands, doing good to all (JP 134)

Make me a channel of Your peace (SOFK 130, JP 161)

Peter and John went to pray (JP 198)

When I needed a neighbour (JP 275)

In everything that I do, show me what Jesus would do
   (JP 391)

It's the little things that show our love for Jesus (JP 403)

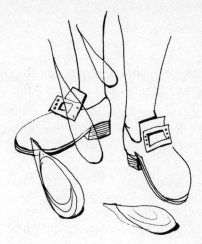

4. The Wrangler

(The story of Galileo Galilei)

Over 400 years ago, a young medical student was given the nickname 'the Wrangler'. The lad's real name was Galileo Galilei and his nickname had nothing to do with the clothes he wore (sixteenth-century Italians had never heard of jeans!). It had to do with the fact that he was always 'wrangling', or arguing, with his teachers.

The trouble was that most of his teachers taught from books written hundreds of years earlier, by a man called Aristotle – books which described what the world was like, how everything worked and why things were the way they were. They expected their students to accept everything in these books without question, but Galileo believed in using his eyes and thinking for himself.

One winter day as he sat in class, bored as usual, Galileo looked out through the narrow window and saw that the sky was heavy with clouds. Suddenly – plop! plop! plop! – hailstones began to pelt down, bouncing off the cobbled courtyard.

The sight reminded him of something he'd noticed in an earlier storm. Two hailstones had landed at his feet – one the size of a large pea, the other smaller. The interesting thing was that they'd hit the ground at the same time.

'Galileo – could you spare me a moment of your attention?' The professor's sarcastic voice interrupted his thoughts.

'Sorry, sir. It's just that I saw something that made me wonder if Aristotle had got it wrong – about big objects always falling faster than small ones, I mean.'

It could have been the start of an interesting discussion, but it wasn't.

'The bigger the object, the faster it falls. That's the rule,' the teacher said stiffly. 'Now could we please get back to today's lesson. . . .'

In the end Galileo decided to give up medicine. But a few years later he was back at his old university, this time as a teacher himself. You can probably guess how his old teachers felt about that. 'Oh no! Not him again.' And sure enough the Wrangler took up where he'd left off, poking holes in Aristotle's thinking. He even went so far as to drop weights, one ten times heavier than the second, from the world-famous leaning tower of Pisa to prove that the heavy one didn't hit the ground ten times more quickly, as they said it should.

Then, in 1610, Galileo designed a telescope that allowed him to see with his own eyes things Aristotle had only imagined. For example, Aristotle had described the surface of the moon. 'It is smooth and polished,' he had said. 'Nothing spoils its perfection.' But when Galileo turned his spy-glass (as he called it) on the moon, what did he see? Certainly no vision of polished smoothness. He saw humps and holes, mountains and valleys. Proof, once again, that Aristotle was mistaken.

But there was more, much more. Aristotle had taught that the planet earth hung quite still at the centre of the universe. But what Galileo saw through his spy-glass convinced him that the earth was moving, and it was the sun that stood still.

He set down his findings in a book called *The Starry Messenger*, which really got people talking. The followers of Aristotle, meanwhile, were out to make trouble. They were careful and sneaky – a letter here, a quiet word there.

'This idea of the earth moving round the sun. It's not what Aristotle teaches – or the Bible,' they said.

Their plan was to get the religious authorities involved in the wrangle. For in those days the religious authorities could make things very nasty for anyone who seemed to be stepping out of line.

Now, the fact was – as Galileo tried to point out – the Bible didn't really teach that the sun moved round the earth. But once the rumours started, the religious authorities decided to crack down. At the height of Galileo's success, they ruled that to believe the earth moved round the sun was against church law.

Overnight Galileo's work became much more difficult and dangerous. Still, he hadn't been christened the Wrangler for nothing.

'I'll write another book,' he thought to himself. 'A book in which different characters have a discussion. One could be a follower of Aristotle, and the other could be more of a scientist. That way I'll keep on the right side of the authorities, because I won't actually say which one I believe.'

It was a clever idea, but the authorities saw straight

through it. Outraged, they banned the book and sentenced Galileo to house imprisonment.

'That's it! We've won!' thought his enemies, as they rubbed their hands with glee.

But they were wrong.

It turned out that banning Galileo's book simply made scholars keener than ever to get their hands on a copy.

And the earth kept right on moving round the sun!

Teaching point

When Jesus opens our eyes spiritually, we may run into opposition, but one day the truth will be plain to all.

Bible reading

John 9:13–41.

Application

After telling the story, link it with John 9:13–41 – the story of the Pharisees making trouble for the man born blind. Bring out the fact that both Galileo and the man born blind uncovered truth. For Galileo it was truth about the universe. For the man born blind it was spiritual truth about who Jesus was and what he could do. The discovery brought him new life and joy, but it also brought trouble and misunderstanding. The same can happen to followers of Jesus today. What helps us stick to our beliefs when the going gets tough? Encourage the group to see that those who hold to the truth win through in the end.

Songs

All things bright and beautiful (JP 6)

Colours of day dawn into the mind (SOFK 14, JP 28)
Come to Jesus, 'He's amazing' (JP 33)
He gave me eyes so I could see (JP 74)
Live, live, live (JP 153)
O Lord my God! When I in awesome wonder (JP 179)
Lord, You are brilliant, champion of champions (JP 423)

FEBRUARY

Work and Play

5. *The Dream Team*

Billy is on the football pitch, happy and excited
He's been picked to play as goalie for the school team –
   Kids United.
But what Billy doesn't realise, as the teams begin to run,
Is that within his **body** a quarrel has begun.
'When goals are saved,' says Billy's **brain**, 'it's mainly
   thanks to me.
Quick thinking makes a goalie, as I'm sure you will agree.'
'No way,' growls Billy's **tummy**. 'You're getting this all
   wrong.
It's eating that makes a goalie. I make Billy strong.'
'It's catching,' yells one of Billy's **hands**. 'It's seeing,' roars
   an **eye**.

'It's balance,' bawls Billy's inner **ear**. 'It's footwork,' his **feet**
   cry.

Then Billy's **brain** has an idea, to prove it is the best.
It decides to go on strike that day and leave thinking to the
   rest.
And Billy's **feet** feel just the same. They decide to pack it
   in.
'We'll leave footwork to the **hands**,' they say. 'And see if
   they can win.'
'And we'll leave seeing to the **ears**,' the **eyes** say with a wink.
'Let them discover for themselves how hard we work to
   blink.'

Billy stands between the posts, waiting to save those
   goals,
And then just as the ball draws near, his **body** parts swop
   roles.
It's a corner to the attacking side. They're lining up to
   shoot.
The striker runs towards the ball and slams it with his
   boot,
And Billy doesn't spot it 'cos he's seeing with his **ears**.
The ball goes in. He's let it through. The opposition cheers.
Seconds pass, and the ball is back in play again,
With attackers charging down the pitch, getting closer all
   the time.
And Billy should be out there, catching the ball before it
   lands.
Instead of which, with his **feet** on strike, he's walking on
   his **hands**.
Upside down, he has no chance of warding off that ball.
The opposition cheer again. They've scored another goal.
And Billy's team-mates swallow hard. Their hopes are
   quickly draining.

The coach yells: 'Billy, concentrate! Remember all your
   training!'
And Billy's **tummy** does its best to get Billy thinking
   straight,
But instead of last week's training Billy remembers what he
   ate.
And the more his **tummy** tries to think, the hungrier he
   feels.
He's no interest in defending. All he can think about is
   meals.
Another ball comes flying past. It's the third goal inside a
   minute.
The outcome of the match is plain: with Billy, the Kids
   can't win it.
'OFF! OFF! OFF!' the supporters chant. 'Billy might look
   cute,
But a tuft of grass could stop more goals. Bring on a sub-
   stitute.'

Billy sits in the changing room, hanging his head in shame.
Poor lad! It's really not his fault. We know who is to
   blame. . .
His **eyes** and **ears**, his **hands** and **feet**, his **tummy** and his **brain**.

Will Billy ever get a chance to save goals for his team?
The answer's yes – because, you see, this story was a dream!
'Wake up, Billy! Breakfast-time,' a voice is heard to say.
And Billy leaps straight out of bed. The real match is today.

Teaching point

Being united in the body of Christ.

Bible reading

1 Corinthians 12:12–27.

Telling the story

Beforehand divide the group into the six parts of Billy's body mentioned in the rhyme, i.e. brain, tummy, hands, feet, eyes and ears. Every time the part they represent is mentioned, they repeat phrases as follows: brain – 'Master mind'; tummy – 'Rumble, rumble'; hands – 'Clap, clap'; feet – 'Stamp, stamp'; eyes – 'Watch it!'; ears – 'Hear, hear!'. When the word 'body' is used, all parts speak together.

Application

After reading the rhyme, ask the group if anyone can remember the name of Billy's school team (Kids United). Hold up a sign with the word 'UNITED' and ask what the word means (together, having the same purpose). Suggest that another name for the church should be 'CHRISTIANS UNITED'. But sometimes instead of being united, Christians let God down by arguing and wanting to be number one – which is really as silly as Billy's feet and eyes and brain deciding to go on strike. Finish by praying that those who follow Jesus would work together and be united in the way that God intends.

Songs

Bind us together, Lord (SOFK 10, JP 17)
Brothers and sisters (JP 21)
A new commandment (SOFK 4, JP 303)
Counting, counting, one, two, three (JP 326)
God loves you, and I love you (SOFK 42, JP 348)
I am the Church (JP 367)

6. *Romeo and Juliet*

(St Valentine's Day)

There is an old tradition that St Valentine's Day is the day birds choose their mates and start nest-building. Here, then, is a story about two love-birds and their nest. The birds were two pet finches called Romeo and Juliet. Davy, their owner, had given them those names because they were totally devoted to each other. Everywhere Juliet went, Romeo would follow. They would feed together and bathe together. And when they perched on a branch they sat so close, they almost seemed to be joined together at the wings.

One day, a few months after putting them into his aviary, Davy poked two pink paper tissues through the wire mesh.

All of a twitter, Romeo and Juliet flew down to investigate. 'What's this? What's this?' they sang.

'It's nesting material,' a wise old budgerigar called Snowy told them. 'Use the tissues to build your nest. Use the nest to lay your eggs. Use your bodies to keep the eggs warm. And before you know it the aviary will be full of new life.'

'New life! Wonderful! We'll start today!' sang Juliet.

'New start today! New start today!' echoed Romeo.

So the two finches threw themselves into nest-building. Within a few days they had lined the wicker nest-basket in the corner of the aviary. The nest was thick and soft, and Juliet laid five beautiful eggs in it.

Now was the time for the finches to sit on their eggs. But to the budgerigar's disgust they continued to fly backwards and forwards adding bits and pieces to their nest.

'We must finish our nest before we sit on our eggs,' Juliet explained.

'Must finish our nest . . . must finish our nest,' echoed Romeo.

The next day they were still flying to and fro.

'We must decorate our nest before we sit on our eggs,' twittered Juliet. 'We need lots of greenery. . . .'

'Need lots of greenery . . . need lots of greenery,' echoed Romeo.

The next day it was feathers that they needed.

'We can't raise chicks in an unfeathered nest!' chirped Juliet, as they fluttered past. 'We want lots of feathers. . . .'

'Want lots of feathers . . . want lots of feathers,' Romeo agreed.

Snowy sighed. 'If you don't sit on your eggs soon, you'll be sorry,' she warned.

But the finches didn't sit on their eggs. Instead, that night, they did something very mean. While Snowy slept, they fluttered over and plucked six white feathers from the budgerigar's tail. 'Silly old bird. She always thinks she knows best,' Juliet cheeped.

'Old bird knows best . . . old bird knows best,' twittered Romeo.

'Honestly, Romeo. Sometimes I think you don't listen to a word I say,' Juliet cut in. 'I didn't say she knows best. I said she was silly.'

The finches hid the feathers at the entrance to the nest-basket. Then, as daylight broke, they fluttered inside to put the finishing touches to the nest. But what was this! Overnight something terrible had happened. Their five beautiful eggs had disappeared.

'Thieves . . . robbers . . . eggnappers . . .' they cried, shooting across the aviary in a terrible flap.

'What's the matter? Has something gone wrong?' Snowy called.

'Our five beautiful eggs have been eggnapped,' cried Juliet.

'There are thieves in the aviary, that's for sure,' Snowy said. 'They stole my tail feathers too.'

Ooops. The finches fluttered to a sudden halt, looking guilty. 'That wasn't thieves – that was us,' admitted Juliet. 'We're sorry. We'll never steal feathers again. So please give us back our eggs.'

'I didn't touch your eggs,' said Snowy. 'But I think I know where they are. Follow me.' And she led the way into the nest-basket.

'There's no point coming here,' Juliet cheeped. 'We told you – the eggs are gone.'

Sure enough the nest looked empty. But that didn't put Snowy off. Deliberately she started scratching down through the tissue paper floor. Deeper and deeper she scratched, until suddenly her claws tapped against something – something smooth and warm and solid.

'Just as I thought,' she cried. 'Your eggs were here all along, buried under a layer of nest.'

Hurrah! In a flash the finches were helping her toss the

paper and feathers and greenery aside. And there the eggs were.

'Oh happy day! Our eggs are safe!' sang Juliet.

And for once Romeo didn't copy her. Instead he spread his wings out over the eggs and sat down.

So it turned out that when Davy came to feed the birds later that morning, he found a very peaceful aviary. Juliet had taken over from Romeo, keeping the eggs warm, while Snowy swung contentedly on her perch. Still Davy couldn't help noticing her missing tail feathers. 'What's been going on, Snowy?' he asked.

But Snowy only winked. Who cared about tail feathers when the aviary would soon be full of new life? And anyway, she was a budgerigar – not a tell-tale tit!

Teaching point

Getting our priorities right.

Bible reading

Luke 10:38–42.

Application

Before telling the story, ask the group about things they have done that week, and list various activities. Ask if anyone sent or received a Valentine card. Lead into the story by saying that there is an old tradition that St Valentine's Day was the day when the birds started to do something, i.e. to build their nests.

Tell the story, then return to the list of activities. Remind the group that Romeo and Juliet made the big mistake of letting one activity – nest-building – stop them doing something more important. In the New Testament story of Mary and Martha, Martha made the same mistake – housework took over (write 'housework' on the list). But Mary got it right. She put God first (write 'time with Jesus' on the list). In the midst of all the different things we do each week, let us remember that staying in touch with God is the most important thing of all.

Songs

Dear Lord and Father of mankind (JP 37)
In our work and in our play (JP 108)
I want to live for Jesus every day (JP 122)
Seek ye first (SOFK 154, JP 215)
The Word of the Lord is planted in my heart (JP 473)

7. Home and Away

(Brownie Thinking Day)

It was a quarter to eight on Monday morning. Drring – Emily's alarm clock rang. 'Time to get up, Emily!' Mrs Martin called.

'Oh bother!' Emily sat up in bed looking grumpy. 'I hate having to get up so early.'

The girl went down for breakfast. Her dad handed her a bowl of steaming porridge. Emily wrinkled her nose. 'We're out of cereal, I'm afraid,' her dad said. 'It's porridge or nothing.'

'Oh bother!' Emily sat down at the table, looking grumpier than ever. 'I hate porridge.'

After breakfast, Emily set off for school. It was a wet morning and she sloshed through puddles gloomily. 'Why does this country have to be so wet!' she grumbled. 'I hate rain.'

At school that morning Miss Ruler gave Emily's class a spelling test. Emily spelled bird B-R-I-D and girl G-R-I-L and boy B-O-G, and Miss Ruler wasn't happy. 'You'll have to stay in at break and write out corrections, Emily,' she said.

'Oh bother!' thought Emily. 'I hate school.'

When Emily finally got home from school, she found her mum rushing round the house in a panic. 'We're having unexpected visitors,' she cried. 'Be a darling and dust the lounge.'

The last thing Emily felt like being was a darling, but she didn't have much choice. She fetched a duster from the cupboard and stomped around the lounge with a face like thunder. 'I hate housework,' she groaned.

After tea Emily got ready for Brownies. Then she went next door to pick up her best friend Sue. Sue was really looking forward to the meeting. Today was Thinking Day and their Guider, Mrs James, had just returned from a trip to Africa.

'She's going to tell us all about the Kenyan Brownies,' Sue cried excitedly. '*And* she said she had a surprise for us. What do you think it could be?'

'Don't know,' growled Emily.

Sue looked puzzled. 'What's the matter with you?'

Emily shrugged, saying, 'I've had a really horrible day.' And she told Sue the whole tale of woe about getting up and porridge and rain and school and housework.

By the time she'd finished, the girls had reached the Brownie Hall. They went inside and soon the Brownie meeting was in full swing. Because it was Thinking Day, Mrs James had organised a special programme to help them think about their Brownie sisters in other lands. The most exciting bit came when they were all seated in the Brownie Ring, and she told them about the Brownies she'd visited in Kenya.

'The Sixes there have animal names,' the Guider explained. 'Their Pack is called a Flock and their leader is called Wise Bird. They play games and work for badges just the same as you do, but they don't have much equipment. So they were really pleased with the pencils and notebooks you sent. What's more, they sent you something back.'

At this Emily and Sue exchanged curious glances. What could it be?

Mrs James held up a bundle of cards. 'Each Brownie in the Kenyan flock made a Thinking Day card for a Brownie in this Pack,' she explained. 'I'll give them out in a minute, but first . . .' she unfolded a thin sheet of paper, 'I want to read you this letter from their leader, Wise Bird.'

Wise Bird's letter was written in rather flowery English, which made Emily smile at first.

'Our beloved Brownie sisters, we greet you most warmly,' she began. Then she went on to describe what life was like for the Brownies in her Flock.

'My Brownies must work very hard,' she explained. 'They get up when the sun rises and help at home, gathering sticks and fetching water.'

Get up at sunrise! Emily's jaw dropped. She knew the sun always rose early in Africa.

'School begins at eight o'clock and when it finishes they have homework and more jobs to do.'

Gosh! They don't get much time to play, Emily thought.

The letter finished with a special request: 'On this Thinking Day we are asking you to pray for us,' Wise Bird wrote. 'It is now already February and the December rains have failed again. In many families there are food shortages with only enough maize and beans for eating every second day. It is hard for the Brownies to work well at school when their tummies are empty. Still they try to learn because they know it is a fine thing to get an education. Please pray with us that the famine will be over soon.'

There was a silence when Mrs James finished reading. All the Brownies were struck by what they had heard – especially Emily. She was remembering how she'd grumbled to Sue about the rain and school and getting up early and having porridge for breakfast and having to help for half an hour at home.

She still had a thoughtful look on her face when Mrs James called her up to collect her Thinking Day card.

'Inside each card you'll find a copy of one of Wise Bird's favourite Bible verses,' the Guider explained. 'It's 1 Thessalonians chapter 5 verse 18: *Give thanks in all circumstances, for this is God's will for you in Christ Jesus.*'

When Emily arrived home that evening, she found that the tea dishes were piled up on the kitchen table, and her mum (who was with the visitors in the lounge) had left her a note. 'Be a darling!' it said. And this time Emily smiled. 'Here's my chance to put Wise Bird's verse into practice,' she said to herself. And she did. As she scraped the leftovers into the dog's dish, she thanked God that everyone had had more than enough to eat. She thanked him for running water as she washed the cups and plates.

And afterwards she had a happy feeling inside – the sort of feeling that comes from doing the right thing. She went up to bed. 'Lord, please send food and rain to my Brownie sisters in Kenya,' she prayed. Then she read through Wise Bird's favourite Bible verse one last time, and turned out the light.

Teaching point

Being thankful to God.

Bible reading

1 Thessalonians 5:16–18.

Application

Beforehand make a poster with a picture of a frowning face which becomes a smiling face when held upside down. Above the frowning face write the words 'Give thanks in all circumstances'. Above the smiling face (i.e. upside down) write 'For this is God's will for you in Christ Jesus'. (If possible have a photocopy for each child.)

After telling the story, hold up the frowning face. Remind the group that this was the way Emily felt on her way to Brownies and ask them why. (Because things had gone wrong that day.) Change the frowning face to the smiling face and say that Emily learned an important lesson at Brownies. What was it? (That even when things went wrong God wanted her to be thankful for all she'd been given.) That is a lesson he wants each of us to learn. Finish by teaching the action rhyme below, changing the frowning face to the smiling face halfway through.

> When we're tempted to complain
> About work and school and food and rain,
> Lord, help us lift our hearts to you
> In thankfulness for all you do.

Songs

Alleluia, alleluia, give thanks to the risen Lord! (SOFK 2, JP 3)

If I were a butterfly (SOFK 74, JP 94)

It's a happy day and I praise God for the weather (SOFK 96, JP 118)

Stand up, clap hands, shout thank You, Lord (JP 225)

Thank You for ev'ry new good morning (JP 230)

Thank You, Jesus, thank You, Jesus (JP 235)

A naggy mum, a grumpy dad, a brother who's a pain (JP 302)

Are you humbly grateful (JP 309)
Even if I don't like the way things went today (JP 330)
Give thanks to the Lord for He is good (JP 345)
When you're feeling good put your thumbs up (JP 496)

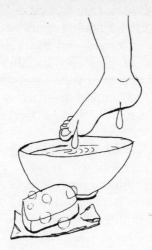

8. Mystery Tour

(A true story from Romania)

Nicky felt bad. She'd been away from home for almost a week, working with a group of Christians in a small Romanian village. They were there to help fix up the village primary school. The trouble was, they had been working round the clock, and, if anything, the school looked worse than when they'd started! Everywhere Nicky turned another half-finished job met her eyes. She was hot because of the blazing sunshine, tired because she'd been working so hard, and worried because the group were due to travel home to Ireland in a couple of days and she couldn't see how they would ever get so many jobs done in such a short space of time.

As she wiped away the sweat from her forehead, she

51

became aware of someone watching her. Nine-year-old Leanna was a dark-eyed gypsy girl, and now she darted forward to pull at Nicky's hand. 'Come,' she said. 'Come.'

At that moment Nicky didn't really want a mystery tour. But Leanna was so bright and eager, she couldn't bring herself to say 'no'. Hoping they wouldn't be going too far, Nicky let the girl take her by the hand and lead her out of the school gates. They walked down a clay path and round a twisty bend in the road, only to arrive at a small cottage, almost hidden from view.

Leanna led the way inside and Nicky guessed this was her home. There was no furniture: no tables, chairs or beds, just a very small room with a concrete floor and box-type ledges on either side. While Nicky sat down on one ledge, Leanna turned to the other, lifted its wooden lid and started rummaging around inside.

She was searching for something – that much was clear. Every now and then she would look round to smile at Nicky and to check that no one was coming. Finally she found what she was looking for: a small object carefully wrapped in brown paper. Before Nicky's curious eyes she pulled back the wrappings, and held out a cracked bar of soap.

'Come,' Leanna said, pulling Nicky to her feet and leading her out into the lane. There she got her companion to sit on a grassy bank, while she skipped over to the pump. Next thing, she was back with an aluminium basin full of water. But it was only when she began to tug at Nicky's sandals that Nicky was able to make sense of it all – the walk, the soap, the pump. . . .

Leanna had brought her here to wash her feet.

Oh dear! At first Nicky didn't want her to do it. Her feet were so dirty, she felt embarrassed. And then she saw the hurt, confused look on the girl's face. 'Why won't you let me help you?' that look said. There was no good reason that Nicky could think of, so she let Leanna take her hot, dusty feet in her hands. Gently the girl washed them in the cool water. She patted them dry with a piece of cloth and replaced Nicky's sandals with care.

A few minutes later they were back in the school classroom – back to the heat and the dust and all those unfinished jobs. But what a difference Leanna's loving action had made. Nicky felt refreshed from top to toe.

Over the next couple of days, work on the school forged ahead. Everything that needed to be done was done; and by the time the team were ready to leave, the building looked as good as new. The roof was tiled, the toilets flushed, the brightly painted classrooms gleamed. What meant most to Nicky, though, wasn't that God had allowed her to do something for the children of this village; it was the way he had used one of the village children to do something very special for her.

As the Irish group climbed into their truck, Leanna stood there eagerly waving goodbye.

'*Multumesc*, Nicky,' she called. (*Multumesc* is Romanian for 'thank you'.) Then she paused for a moment, clearly remembering who was *really* behind it all.

'No,' she corrected herself with a big smile. '*Multumesc*, Jesus!'

Teaching point

God wants us to serve one another.

Bible reading

John 13:3–5, 12–16.

Application

While telling the story, produce soap, a basin and a towel as visual aids. Afterwards say that these things could also be used to illustrate a Bible story. Can anyone think what story it is? (Jesus washing the disciples' feet.) Read John 13:3–5, 12–16. Point out that Jesus asked his followers to wash one another's feet – in other words, to serve one another, just as Leanna and Nicky did. Encourage the group to think of some ways they can serve others. Finish by teaching the action rhyme (below).

Action rhyme

> I serve you and you serve me
> That's the way that it should be
> That's what God would have us do
> You serve me, and I serve you.

(Youngsters get into pairs A and B. During first two lines A does something for B, and during the second two lines B does something for A)

Songs

A boy gave Jesus five loaves and two fish (JP 1)
Have you seen the pussycat, sitting on the wall? (SOFK 53, JP 73)
I'm very glad of God (JP 107)
Jesus' hands were kind hands, doing good to all (JP 134)
We really want to thank You, Lord (SOFK 179, JP 268)
When I needed a neighbour (JP 275)
Lord we ask now to receive Your blessing (JP 301)
A new commandment (SOFK 4, JP 303)
God loves you and I love you (SOFK 42, JP 348)
It's the little things that show our love for Jesus (JP 403)

MARCH
Family Life

9. On the Shelf

Once upon a time there was a family of Russian dolls. They were called Blue, Red, Pea-green, Purple and Pink. Blue was the biggest. Pink was the smallest. And they all lived inside each other on Mrs Honey's bookcase.

During the day they kept quite still – as all good ornaments should. But at night it was a different story. The minute Mrs Honey's grandfather clock struck twelve, Blue would pop his top. Out would jump the four smaller dolls, and they would all play away to their hearts' content. Then, as dawn broke, Blue would call: 'Time to be one.' And Pink would pop into Purple, Purple would jump into Pea-green, Pea-green would leap into Red, and Red would hop into Blue. And by the time Mrs Honey came down for breakfast, they would be just the way she'd left them on the shelf.

But behind their painted smiles life didn't always run smoothly for the Russian dolls. Pea-green was terribly moody.

'It isn't fair. Why am I always in the middle?' he used to shout. 'Why can't we change things so that Blue and Red are inside me?'

'The Toymaker didn't design us that way,' Red tried to explain. 'We wouldn't fit.'

'Toymaker! What Toymaker? I don't believe in any Toymaker!' Pea-green would say, stamping off in a huff.

Not only had he stopped believing in the Toymaker, he'd started playing a dangerous game. He called it super-mega-rock-and-roll.

It was exciting.

It was nerve-wracking.

And one day it went too far. To and fro, to and fro, faster and faster, Pea-green rocked. Then – wheeeee – he rolled himself forward. Whoooooo. He lost control. Whaaaaaaah. He gave a last desperate cry and disappeared off the edge of the shelf.

What now? Blue, Red, Purple and Pink were almost beside themselves with worry. They leaned as far as they dared over the edge, peering down into the darkness. 'Pea-green! Pea-green! Are you all right?' they called. But there was no reply.

By this stage it was well past 'Time to be one'. There was nothing else for it. Slowly and sadly Pink climbed into Purple, Purple climbed into Red, and Red climbed into Blue. They looked exactly the same on the outside, but now instead of fitting together snugly there was a horrible empty space where Pea-green used to be.

Pea-green, meanwhile, had ended up under the bookcase. And try as he would, he couldn't get out. The pile of the living-room carpet was impossible to roll on. The hours

ticked by, and he remained trapped in this murky under-
world, growing more and more depressed. He felt sure that
no one would ever find him, which meant he would be there
for ever – or worse, the mice would turn him into sawdust
with their gnawing teeth. 'Oh, this is awful! How I wish I was
back in the middle!' Pea-green moaned.

And then something quite amazing happened.

The door opened and Mrs Honey walked into the room.
This in itself wasn't amazing. Mrs Honey owned the house,
so she walked into the room quite often. The amazing thing
was she had brought Jane from across the road into the room
with her, and they had come to see the Russian dolls.

'A Toymaker made them for me when I was a child,' the
old lady explained as she lifted them down off the bookcase.

She opened Blue up and set him on the coffee table. Then
she opened Red and found Purple smiling up at her. 'My
goodness!' she exclaimed. 'I can't think how it's happened,
but one of my dolls has disappeared. The Toymaker made a
special middle doll – a green one. And now it's gone.'

This gave Jane an idea for a game. 'Let's play hunt the
doll,' she cried.

You can probably guess what happened next.

After ten minutes of searching – through cupboards,
behind cushions, under chairs – Jane gave a squeal of
delight. 'I've found it. It's in here, under the bookcase, Mrs
Honey. I've found your little green doll.'

What a relief! Mrs Honey and Jane had two big slices of
chocolate cake each to celebrate.

And that night the Russian dolls celebrated too. They
played rock and roll (though not the super-mega variety!)
and Pea-green told them about his adventure. 'It was cool –
sort of,' he said. 'But I'm glad to be home.'

'Time to be one,' smiled Blue, and they were back to their
usual routine. Pink popped into Purple, Purple jumped into
Pea-green, Pea-green leapt into Red, and Red hopped into

Blue. And there they were – a family made to fit together, all happily back together on the shelf.

Teaching point

God has made us to fit together in human families and in the family of the church.

Bible reading

Ephesians 3:14–15.

Application

After telling the story, show the children either a set of Russian dolls or another toy such as a jigsaw which has been made so that the pieces fit together. Then explain that God has made us to fit together in human families and in the church family. In the story, the Russian dolls' family life was unhappy for a while. Ask the group to say why. (Because of Pea-green's behaviour.) Selfish behaviour in family life always hurts other members. But God can help us put things right, so that we live together in the loving way that he intends.

Songs

Father I place into Your hands (SOFK 28, JP 42)
Have you seen the pussycat, sitting on the wall? (SOFK 53, JP 72)
He's got the whole wide world in His hands (JP 78)
In our work and in our play (JP 108)
It's me, it's me, it's me, O Lord (JP 119)
Whether you're one or whether you're two (JP 284)
A naggy mum, a grumpy dad, a brother who's a pain (JP 302)

Counting, counting, one, two, three (JP 326)
God loves you and I love you (SOFK 42, JP 348)
It's not very nice saying 'Na na na na na na' (JP 401)
Sometimes I'm naughty (JP 460)

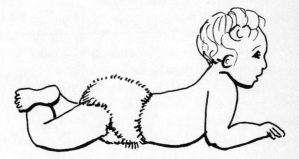

10. Talcum Powder and Safety Pins

(A true story for the birth of a child)

Missionary mum, Joy Molyneux, was delighted when her third son, Gordon, was out of nappies. What a relief! No more nappy buckets, no more rubber pants, no more safety pins! By now you've probably worked out that we're talking about the old-fashioned sort of nappies here. Joy used them for the simple reason that fifty years ago, when this story happened, modern nappies hadn't been invented.

As Gordon got bigger, Joy gave all his nappies and baby things away. She and her husband didn't expect to have any more children. Babies were hard work, and Joy already had more than enough to do. As well as looking after her three boys, she was nursing in the mission hospital and teaching in the primary school. Callers also kept her busy. From the

moment the sun peeped over the hill-tops they would begin
to arrive on her doorstep looking for help: 'Mother, I need a
patch for my shirt.'

'Mother, can you give me a tin for my rice?'

'Mother, make me a pair of shorts.'

In all her work Joy was supported by an older unmarried
missionary called Auntie Ko. Auntie Ko was like an adopted
granny, always ready to step in and act as a baby-sitter, no
matter what time of day or night Joy had to go out.

And then one day Auntie Ko noticed that Joy was in a very
bad mood, marching around the house with a face like
thunder.

'What's the matter? Why are you so cross?' the older missionary asked.

Joy took a deep breath. 'I've just found out I'm going to
have another baby and I'm not one bit pleased about it,' she
cried. 'My husband is overworked, and I'm run off my feet.
I don't even have any baby clothes. . . .'

Another baby! Auntie Ko looked concerned. 'It will be
very bad for the child if you go around so cross and
unhappy,' she said firmly. 'You must sort this out with God.'

'That's easy for you to say. You don't know what it's like,'
Joy sighed, but deep down she knew that Auntie Ko was
right. Leaving the older woman to mind the children, she
made her way to a quiet, shady spot among the palm trees
and started to pray. She asked God to forgive her for being
so angry, and to change how she felt.

As she prayed, the anger went. Soon she was at peace, and
she found herself asking God for something special. 'Lord,
you know I've given all my baby things away. So please show
your love and forgiveness by making sure my new baby has
everything it needs.'

Less than two weeks later a letter arrived. It had travelled
thousands of miles from Joy's mother, Lillian, who lived in
South Africa, and it contained some surprising news. Lillian

knew nothing about Joy's situation, but she was writing to say that she'd met up with a young Christian woman who was very keen to give away four parcels of brand new baby clothes. 'She wants a missionary working in your area to have them. Do you know anyone who is expecting a baby?' Lillian asked.

Did she know anyone expecting a baby!

'I certainly do,' Joy wrote back excitedly. 'Me!'

So it turned out that when Joy's fourth son, David, was born, the contents of those four big parcels were waiting for him in the wardrobe. God had sent everything he could possibly need – from nappies and nightwear, right down to talcum powder and safety pins. But there was more. When his proud parents brought him to church for a service of dedication, God gave them a wonderful promise from his word: 'All your sons will be taught by the Lord, and great will be your children's peace,' they read (Isaiah 54:13). And hearing that promise, Joy realised that for David the clothes were just the beginning. His future would be like his wardrobe – packed full of blessings from God.

Teaching point

God wants to help us care for the babies and young children in our human families and in the church family too.

Bible reading

Mark 10:13–16.

Application

After telling the story, produce a packet of disposable nappies and ask the group to tell you some of the other things babies need today. Make a note of suggestions. Then ask what babies and little children need most of all. (To be loved.) Sometimes we feel cross when a baby is crying or when a younger child is pestering us. That is when we need to remember how Jesus welcomed small children, and how, today, he can help us show them his love.

Extra information

Joy and Colin Molyneux served God in the Belgian Congo for twenty-one years. Their four sons all became followers of Christ, working as missionaries in different parts of Africa.

Action chorus

In a situation where a new baby has been brought into the church family for the first time, the action chorus below may be sung. (Tune: 'God rest ye merry gentlemen')

> A baby needs nursing
> A baby needs to be fed
> A baby needs bathing
> A baby needs a bed
> A baby is a precious gift
> A baby makes us glad
> We give thanks in the family, the family of God
> We give thanks in the family of God. (Hurrah!)

(During the first four lines, the children mime looking after a baby. In line six they jump or clap for joy. After the refrain they cheer.)

Songs

Father I place into Your hands (SOFK 28, JP 42)
God sent His Son, they call Him Jesus (JP 58)

Jesus died for all the children (JP 132)
Jesus loves me! This I know (JP 140)
Heavenly Father, we would sing out Your praise (JP 358)
Kids under construction (JP 414)
Thank You for the love that our mums give to us each day
(JP 467)

11. Secrets

(Mothering Sunday)

Seven-year-old Harry kept losing things. He lost pieces from jigsaws, and counters from board games. He lost pencils and rubbers and lunchboxes. 'He'd lose his head if it wasn't screwed on,' his mum would say.

Harry's mum never lost anything – or so Harry believed.

And then, the day before his eighth birthday, he noticed his mum acting strangely. She had come upstairs to put away the ironing. Nothing strange about that! The strange thing was the way she acted when Harry followed her onto the landing and asked about the box she was putting into the airing cupboard – the way she looked secretive. 'What's inside that box is none of your business, Harry Jones,' she said. 'And don't you go poking your nose in.'

When his mum had gone back downstairs, Harry slipped out onto the landing. He opened the airing cupboard door and took a good look at the box. He didn't touch it of course, because his mum had told him not to. He just wanted to see whether the lid was going up and down. Because if the lid was going up and down that would mean there was a puppy moving about inside.

Harry was hoping to get a puppy for his birthday. He'd wanted a dog of his own for *ages*. His mum already had a dog, a terrier called Tinker. But there was no fun left in Tinker. He was old, stiff, deaf and blind, and Harry called him Stinker because . . . well, you can probably guess why.

So the boy stared at the cardboard box, hoping against hope that he would see signs of life inside.

He didn't.

Disgusted, Harry made his way downstairs and out into the garden. He knew the box in the airing cupboard must hold his birthday present. What else would his mum be trying to hide? And if it was his birthday present, he now also knew he wasn't getting a puppy. His mum must have decided that he couldn't be trusted with a dog of his own.

'It isn't fair,' Harry thought angrily. 'If Mum got me a puppy, I wouldn't lose it. She just won't give me a chance.' He looked round the garden and there was Tinker sound asleep in his kennel. 'That dog is a waste of space!' the boy thought. He saw something else too. A catapult. The catapult didn't belong to Harry. It belonged to his cousin Mark. But Harry knew how to use it. He picked up a stone, slipped it into the catapult, pulled back the elastic and fired. He was aiming at the kennel, hoping to give Tinker a shock. But instead of hitting against the wood, the stone struck the old dog sharply between the eyes.

'Yap!' Tinker yelped loudly and struggled to his feet.

Poor old dog! 'I didn't mean to hit him,' Harry told himself. 'It was the stupid catapult's fault. Mark shouldn't leave catapults lying around.' He buried the catapult in the flower bed and ran back into the house.

The next morning – the morning of Harry's birthday – the boy came down for breakfast to find his mum looking tearful. 'Happy birthday, darling,' she sniffed. 'Uncle John will be round soon with your present. It's a Labrador pup. Your grandad has just been over to take Tinker away.'

'Take Tinker away! What do you mean?' Harry cried.

Sadly his mum explained that Tinker would be happier living with Grandpa from now on. 'I want you to have a dog of your own,' she said. 'But it wouldn't be fair to expect Tinker to share his home with a pup. So giving Tinker to Grandpa is the best thing to do.' She gave herself a little shake and smiled. 'Now what are we going to call your new pup?'

Harry called his pup Goldie. She was gorgeous – a cuddly, crazy, licking bundle of fun, and if it hadn't been for Tinker, Harry would have been over the moon. The trouble was, even though he was normally so good at losing things, he couldn't lose the memory of Tinker's last afternoon in the garden. It was like watching a video every time he shut his eyes. He kept hearing the old dog yelp and seeing him shake his injured head.

Meanwhile Goldie got up to all sorts of mischief. She ran off with so many slippers and toys that all of a sudden Harry had a great excuse when he lost anything. 'Goldie must have taken it,' he would say. Then one day Harry and his mum looked out of the kitchen window to see the pup furiously digging up the flower bed.

'Bad dog . . . stop that at once . . .' they ran out, shouting.

Goldie rushed to meet them. She had something in her mouth – something she'd just dug up. Proudly she dropped the catapult at Harry's feet.

Immediately Harry remembered. 'I'm sorry . . . I'm really sorry. . . .' He buried his face in his hands.

'Sorry for what?' his mum said, looking at him in amazement.

Then Harry told her exactly what had happened the afternoon before his birthday – from the moment he'd seen the box in the airing cupboard to the moment he'd hit Tinker with the stone. 'I'm sorry. I'm really sorry,' he kept saying.

His mum gave him a hug. 'God knows that, Harry. Just ask him to forgive you and he'll take the guilty feeling away.'

So Harry did. And immediately the horrible guilty feeling went.

What a relief! But there was still one little question niggling in the back of the boy's mind.

'Mum, what *do* you keep in that box?' he asked.

'Oh *that*!' she shrugged. 'It was silly of me not to tell you the truth when you asked. The thing is, I've ticked you off so often about losing things, I didn't want to admit to losing things myself.'

'What do you mean?'

'Come upstairs and I'll show you.'

They went upstairs, with Harry's mum muttering on about how it was the washing machine's fault really, and Harry getting more and more confused. Finally they reached the airing cupboard where Harry's mum handed Harry the box. 'I keep hoping their partners will turn up,' she sighed.

Holding his breath, the boy lifted the lid.

And there was Mum's guilty secret: half a dozen odd socks!

Teaching point

Saying 'sorry' to one another and to God.

Bible reading

1 John 1:5–10.

Telling the story

Tell the story using a shoebox as a visual aid. Open it and take out the socks at the end.

Application

Before telling the story, hold up a card saying 'super-mum'. Talk to the group about all the different ways their mums are super, and say you have a story for them about a boy and his mum. After telling the story, hold up the card again and say that one thing this story illustrates is that nobody is perfect – not even a super-mum. We can all have guilty secrets. Finally hold up a card with 1 John 1:9 copied onto it. Explain that this is God's answer to guilty secrets. He wants us to say 'sorry' and truly mean it. And he is always ready to forgive.

Songs

God is so good (JP 53)
I'm special (SOFK 92, JP 106)
Jesus bids us shine (JP 128)
Search me, O God, and know my heart today (JP 212)
All you have to do is to ask the Lord (JP 307)
Sometimes I'm naughty (JP 460)
Sorry Lord, for all the things (JP 463)
Thank You for the love that our mums give to us each day
   (JP 467)
The Spirit lives to set us free (JP 472)

12. No Place Like Home

It is springtime and a band of travellers are walking towards Jerusalem. They are ordinary folk, all from Galilee, all taking time off from their normal jobs to celebrate the Passover. (That's a special Jewish festival, a bit like Christmas for us.)

Mary, Joseph and twelve-year-old Jesus are part of the group.

Joseph is with the other men. The Passover gives him a welcome break from mending yokes and ploughs. It also gives him a chance to talk. He and his companions are grumbling in low voices about the Romans, who've taken over their land, wondering how long it will be before God sends the Messiah to deliver them. 'Get rid of the Romans,' they mutter. 'And all our problems will be solved.'*

71

Mary, meanwhile, is with a group of women. Because in her day women don't work outside the home, the Passover gives Mary a welcome break from the loom and the water jugs. She too is glad of the chance to chat to her friends. Right now they're talking about the secret of making a perfect barley loaf: 'Knead it, shape it, pat it, bake it.'*

While this is going on, Jesus is with the other boys of his own age. Very soon he will become a 'Son of the Law', which means he will be expected to play a 'grown-up' part back home in his church (or synagogue). This Passover gives him time to prepare for what lies ahead. But it's also a great adventure – travelling so far from home, sleeping out at night under the starry sky. At the moment he and his friends are running races. 'Last one to the top of the hill is a tax-collector! Ready, get set, GO!' a voice calls.*

The travellers spend the next few days among thousands of Jews from all over the country. They offer their sacrifices in the Temple. They share in the Passover meal. All too soon, though, the festival is over and they must return to Galilee. Once again the company take to the road, travelling in the same order as before – women and small children first,* then the men,* with the older children moving about between the groups.*

'Funny!' thinks Mary, as she leaves Jerusalem behind. 'I haven't seen Jesus lately. He must be with his father.'

'Funny!' thinks Joseph, as he brings up the rear with the other men. 'I haven't seen Jesus lately. He must be with his mother.'

You can imagine their horror when they meet up at the camp-site at the end of the day.

'Where's Jesus?'

'I thought he was with you.'

'No, I haven't seen him since this morning. I thought he was with you.'

They question their friends and relatives, only to discover that no one has seen Jesus since they left Jerusalem. Oh dear!

What could have happened to him? Picturing all sorts of disasters, Mary and Joseph head straight back the way they've come.

They spend one of the worst days of their lives searching the city streets. 'Have you seen a twelve-year-old boy with a Galilean accent?' Joseph asks the same question over and over again – and meets with a blank look every time. There have been *thousands* of visitors to the city for the Passover. How can anyone be expected to remember one ordinary* country lad? As the sun sinks lower, Mary and Joseph grow more and more desperate. Mary is afraid her son may have drowned in one of the city pools, while Joseph is secretly worried that he might have been run over by a camel.

And then, at last, it hits them. The Temple. They haven't checked there.

Hoping against hope, they enter the courtyard of the magnificent Temple building. They walk past the money-changers, past the pens of animals and cages of birds, along the steps, under the shady porchway – and there he is! What a relief! Their long-lost son is sitting on the steps, deep in conversation with the religious teachers. Jesus has spent the last three days in the Temple courtyard, listening to what the scribes and rabbis have to say. The strange thing is – and this is what really hurts Mary – he doesn't seem the least bit bothered about his parents. How *could* he have been so thoughtless? 'Why did you do this to us?' she cries. 'Your father and I were hunting for you everywhere. We've been worried sick.'

Jesus gives her a look. It's a look of love and respect. But also of surprise.

'Didn't you know I was sure to be in my Father's house?' he asks.

And everyone falls silent, including the scribes and rabbis. What is it about this boy? He looks so ordinary.* But never before have they come across a twelve-year-old who seems to know God in such an extraordinary way.

The family return to Galilee. Joseph gets back to the carpenter's bench. Mary gets back to baking. Jesus carries on being an obedient son. And that's the end of the story – except to say that it isn't by chance that Jesus is growing up in this ordinary* house, helping Mary with the housework, learning carpentry from Joseph and larking about with his friends. It's part of God's plan. For God has deliberately chosen this simple Galilean home to be the place where he will fill his Son's life with his presence and power.

Home can be that sort of place for us too.

Teaching point

Knowing God as Father makes an extraordinary difference to ordinary life.

Bible reading

Luke 2:41–52.

Telling the story

Before telling the story, divide the group into three: 'men', 'women' and 'children'. As they are introduced in the opening paragraphs each group repeats a phrase as follows: men – 'Get rid of the Romans'; women – 'Knead it, shape it, pat it, bake it'; children – 'Ready, get set, GO'. The groups repeat these phrases again at the point when the men, women and children leave Jerusalem. Thereafter they all repeat their phrases together every time they hear the word 'ordinary'.

Application

After telling the story hold up a poster of somewhere that the children would be likely to find exciting (e.g.

Disneyland). Then remind them that for twelve-year-old Jesus the Temple in Jerusalem was the most exciting place in the world. But even though he stayed there a little longer than his parents expected, he still went back home. Ask the group about the ordinary everyday places that are part of their lives (home, school, church, etc.). Aim to show that these are the places where God wants us to fill our lives with his love.

Songs

By blue Galilee Jesus walked of old (JP 23)
God is our guide, our light and our deliverer (JP 56)
Have you seen the pussycat, sitting on the wall?
  (SOFK 53, JP 72)
He gave me eyes so I could see (JP 74)
New every morning is the love (JP 171)
Thank You for ev'ry new good morning (JP 230)
Get up out of bed (JP 343)
Maybe you can't draw or sing or be a football star (JP 429)

APRIL

The Easter Story

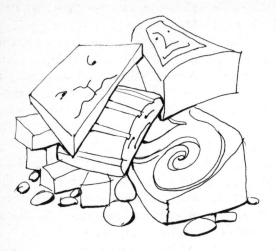

13. The Stones Cry Out

(Palm Sunday)

A kerbstone, a paving-stone and a corner-stone once met on a rubbish tip. All three were chipped and broken, and all three felt they'd been treated very badly. In fact you could say that they had 'chips' the size of elephants on their shoulders.

'Humans are so ungrateful,' grumbled the kerbstone. 'I spent my working days at the edge of a pavement, letting them walk all over me. I never tripped anyone up. And what thanks did I get? None. A gang of men with pick-axes came along and smashed the pavement to bits.'

The paving-stone's life had been unhappy too. 'I spent my working days in the middle of a railway platform, having human luggage dumped on top of me,' it complained. 'I always kept perfectly still, but I got no thanks either. One

78

day a gang of men with cranes came along and turned the station into a multi-storey car-park.'

The corner-stone felt its experience with humans had been worst of all. 'I spent fifty years on the corner of a bridge,' it wailed. 'You have no idea what I had to put up with . . . humans in cars and lorries driving across me at all hours of the day and night. I often felt like crumbling, but instead I stood firm. Did a single human being ever thank me for my efforts? Huh! Does cement bounce?! I give fifty years' service and what happens? A gang of men with bulldozers knock down the bridge – that's what.'

One day, as the three stones were talking about the Unfairness of It All, the same thought struck them. Enough was enough! It was time to call for revolution; time to send rocks and pebbles everywhere collapsing, tumbling and smashing down on their human masters.

There was just one problem. A revolution needed a leader.

The paving-stone looked at the corner-stone, and the corner-stone looked at the kerbstone, but somehow none of them felt up to the job.

And then, suddenly, they remembered that right at the bottom of the rubbish tip lay an Ancient Stone – a stone that had been around for thousands of years. So off they tumbled, down over the piles of rubbish, to talk to it. 'We're planning to overthrow the Kingdom of the World,' they explained. 'All we need is a wise old leader like you. . . .'

As they spoke, the Ancient Stone's pure whiteness shone in the sun and the wisdom of ages gleamed in his veins.

'But a Great Leader has already overthrown the Kingdom of the World,' it observed calmly. 'It happened when I was a young marble hunk lying loose on the road to Jerusalem. I was there to see him ride through the city gates.'

'You're telling us this Great Leader rode into Jerusalem on his war horse and smashed human power to bits?' the kerb-stone cried.

'No,' said the Ancient Stone. 'He rode in on a donkey, and he let himself be smashed.'

'He let himself be smashed!' The stones rolled back in wonder. 'But that doesn't make sense.'

'It makes spiritual sense,' said the Ancient Stone. 'He'd come to set up a Kingdom of Love, you see; and you don't do that with weapons of war. No, he knew the only way to do it was by letting humans break open his body and shed his blood.'

There was a long silence after this. Beneath their broken surfaces the stones' bitter anger was melting away.

'I'd like to hear more about this King and his Kingdom of Love,' the corner-stone said at last.

'What I was wondering was whether he had anything to say about stones?' the paving-stone added wistfully.

At this the Ancient Stone started to twinkle. 'Funny you should ask that. The day he rode into Jerusalem, the religious authorities tried to get him to keep his followers quiet. And he turned round and told them that if the people stopped cheering, the stones would cry out.'

'No! He said *that*! About *us*!' The three stones almost cracked with excitement.

'Those were his words,' the Ancient Stone said.

'Well, we weren't there then,' said the kerbstone. 'But we can make up for it now!'

So they did. 'Hosanna! Hosanna! Hosanna!' they cheered.

And next thing there was a sound like rumbling thunder, as stones all over the rubbish tip joined in.

Teaching point

Christ's purpose in riding into Jerusalem.

Bible reading

Luke 19:29–40.

Application

Luke 19:29–40 should be read before the story is told. After telling it, show the group a picture of a cheering crowd and explain how when Jesus rode into Jerusalem he was welcomed with great enthusiasm. The problem was that the people shouting 'Hosanna', or 'Hurrah', hadn't a clue why he was there. Ask the group why they think God sent Jesus into the world. Aim to bring out the fact that he had come to mend people's broken relationship with God. Finish by teaching and singing the action song below.

Action rhyme/song *(can be sung to tune of 'At the name of Jesus')*

> Hosanna, Hosanna,
> Hear the people cheer.
> Riding on a donkey,
> See the King appear.
> Riding to Jerusalem
> In lowliness and love;
> Jesus the Messiah,
> Sent from heaven above.

(Children tap empty cartons on floor to create the rhythm of hoof-beats throughout)

Songs

At the name of Jesus (JP 13)
Children of Jerusalem (JP 24)
Ride on, ride on in majesty (JP 209)
Sing we the King who is coming to reign (JP 218)
We have a King who rides on a donkey (JP 264)

Going up to Jerusalem (JP 354)
Make way, make way (SOFK 131, JP 427)
The journey of life may be easy, may be hard (JP 468)
Easter jubilation (SOFK 26)

14. *Trespassers Prosecuted*

(Holy Week)

One morning a poor shoeless lad called Robbie Robertson set off into the countryside carrying a bucket. His plan was to gather enough blackberries to fill his bucket to the brim and then sell the fruit at the market, so that his parents would have the money to pay the rent. But after two hours of trudging up and down country lanes, Robbie had hardly enough blackberries to cover the bottom of the bucket.

'I'm wasting my time. I might as well go home,' he sighed.

And then he spotted it: a patch of brambles weighed down with clusters of huge, ripe, juicy blackberries. There was just one problem. These blackberries weren't growing along the side of the road. They were growing in a field – a field belonging to Robbie's landlord, Sir Donald McDuff – and there was a sign on the gate which said: 'Trespassers prosecuted'.

Robbie knew this sign meant that anyone caught in the field would get into serious trouble, but his parents needed money badly, and this seemed like his one chance of getting it. So he climbed over a broken-down part of the fence, ran to the brambles and started picking.

In next to no time his bucket was full.

Robbie was just congratulating himself when he heard footsteps. Someone was coming. He looked round and saw Old Albert, Sir Donald McDuff's handyman, heading towards him across the field.

Immediately the boy tried to escape, but it was difficult. The brambles caught in his hair and tore at his clothes. Then – disaster! – he trod on a nail. 'Oww!' He sank to the ground, groaning and clutching his injured foot. Next thing he knew, Old Albert was towering over him – a huge, rugged mountain of a man.

Between the pain of his foot and his fear of being punished, Robbie was in a sorry state. 'Please . . . please don't hand me over to Sir Donald,' he begged.

For some reason, instead of answering, Old Albert just stood there staring at the thorny length of bramble caught in Robbie's hair.

'Do you know what I'm thinking?' he said at last.

The boy shook his head.

'I'm thinking my master felt the prick of thorns on his head.'

Old Albert leaned forward and gently removed the thorns. Then he knelt down, took a handkerchief out of his pocket and started to bandage Robbie's foot.

'Do you know what I'm thinking?' he asked again.

Again Robbie shook his head.

'I'm thinking my master felt the pain of nails in his feet.'

By now Robbie had worked out that when Old Albert

talked about his master, he didn't mean Sir Donald McDuff. Sir Donald had never felt the prick of thorns on his head, or the pain of nails in his feet. No. Old Albert was talking about someone else, and Robbie had been at church often enough to know who that someone else was. What's more, he actually remembered something the minister had said – something which, now he found himself caught red-handed with a bucket of stolen blackberries beside a 'Trespassers prosecuted' notice, suddenly seemed like good news.

'Old Albert, I've heard your master forgives trespassers,' he said. 'Is that right?'

'Aye, laddie.' The old handyman's eyes lit up. 'My master forgives trespassers of every size and description.'

Robbie's relief was cut short by the sound of hoof-beats. Cloppity cloppity clop. A black horse was coming down the lane, ridden by . . . Sir Donald. 'Help!' Robbie paled. 'I'll be punished now for sure.'

But Robbie was reckoning without Old Albert.

As Sir Donald approached the fence, the handyman lifted Robbie's bucket and strolled over to the blackberry patch, where he set the bucket down and stood beside it, bending over the brambles.

'Albert! What do you think you are doing?' roared Sir Donald. He was so outraged by what he thought he saw that he didn't even notice Robbie. 'I pay you to mend fences,' he continued, 'not to steal the fruit from my land. You're sacked.' And away he went.

Robbie was left open-mouthed in amazement. In fact his whole expression was a gaping question-mark.

Why? Why had Old Albert taken the blame?

The old handyman came over and sat beside him. It was almost as if he could read Robbie's mind.

'I'll tell you why, laddie,' he explained simply. 'My master took the blame for me.'

The pair were still talking about this half an hour later

when Sir Donald came back. And this time the landowner wasn't looking angry, he was looking worried. He'd just realised that his wife would be furious with him for sacking Old Albert, and he was hoping it wasn't too late to put things right.

'I'm sorry I lost my temper, Albert,' he began with an oily smile. 'The fact is you are a wonderful handyman and you have served my family well for many years. So please forget what I said.'

Old Albert winked at Robbie.

'I'll forget it gladly, Sir Donald,' he nodded, 'on one condition. I'm thinking a man my age could do with an assistant. And I'm thinking it would be a very good thing if you were to give young Robbie Robertson here the job.'

'Oh . . . very well,' said Sir Donald, who could see he had no choice.

'And I'm thinking the lad could do with a week's pay in advance,' the handyman added shrewdly.

Rolling his eyes, Sir Donald dipped into his pocket and handed Robbie a silver coin.

So it came about that, thanks to Old Albert, instead of being punished Robbie went home with a full-time job and the rent money. Best of all, though, the lad had a wonderful sense of forgiveness. He understood now, about the thorns and the nails and an innocent man taking the blame. He was starting afresh, with a spiritual fortune – all thanks to Old Albert's master.

Teaching point

When Jesus died on the cross, he took the blame for us.

Bible reading

Matthew 27:27–31.

Application

Before telling the story, hold up a 'Trespassers prosecuted' sign and ask what the words mean. Draw attention to the wider meaning of the word 'trespasser', i.e. one who sins or breaks the law.

After telling the story, ask the group the following questions: Who *was* Old Albert's master? Why did Old Albert say that his master had felt the prick of thorns on his brow and the pain of nails in his feet? What did Old Albert mean when he said that his master took the blame for him? (When Jesus died on the cross he took the blame for everyone who has broken God's law.) Point out that we are all trespassers in the sense that we have all broken God's law. By rights this means we should be fearful and guilty. But instead we can have a wonderful sense of God's forgiveness, thanks to what Jesus has done.

Songs

Come and praise the Lord our King (JP 34)
God sent His Son, they call Him Jesus (JP 58)
He paid a debt He did not owe (JP 77)
He was pierced (SOFK 56)
I met You at the cross (JP 103)
It is a thing most wonderful (JP 117)
Oh the love that drew salvation's plan! (JP 181)
Thank You for the cross (SOFK 159)
One day when heaven was filled with His praises (JP 187)
Praise Him! Praise Him! Jesus our blessed Redeemer!
(JP 203)
Saviour of the world, thank You for dying on the cross
(JP 216)
To God be the glory! Great things He has done! (JP 259)
Sorry Lord, for all the things (JP 463)

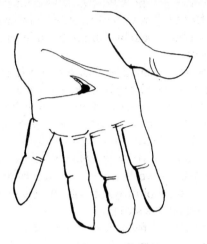

15. Facing Facts

(Easter Sunday)

Hello. My name is Thomas. I was one of Jesus' twelve disciples, and I'm here today because I believe facts are important.

Now I can tell by the look of you that you're a sensible bunch – heads screwed on, feet firmly on the ground. I like that. I always tried to keep my own feet on the ground when I was on earth. I remember once when Jesus was talking to us disciples about heaven. 'You know the way to the place where I am going,' says he. Well, the rest of the disciples sat around nodding blankly. I was the only one to speak up.

'Lord,' I said, 'we don't know *where* you're going, so how can we know the way?'

'*I* am the way,' said Jesus. But he still hadn't told us where he was going.

I was still wondering where he was going when he went! He went in front of crowds of people, with nails in his hands and a great gaping spear-wound in his side. He was crucified, in other words.

Me, I tried to be sensible about it. It might have been the end of all my hopes. I might have seen the last of the most wonderful person I'd ever known. I might be feeling like I'd just been crucified myself inside, but I did my best to face facts. And this meant that when Mary Magdalen came round, the Sunday after it happened, glowing like a lamp and yelling: 'He's alive!' I was a total wet blanket. 'She's hallucinating,' I said bluntly. 'If Jesus' body has gone, it's because someone has stolen it.'

I took myself off for a long walk then. I mean, I felt I needed Mary's excitement like a hole in my level head. Jesus was dead. That was that. End of story.

Except the rest of the disciples had other ideas. They tracked me down the next morning, all as radiant as Mary. 'You missed him, Tom. Jesus appeared to us yesterday evening,' they cried.

I suppose I could have played along with it. I could have turned round and hugged them and let my hopes run wild. But that just wasn't my style. I was facing facts, remember. And every grey cell in my brain told me that people don't die for three days and then come back to life again. It simply *isn't done*! 'Look,' I said, 'unless I see the nail marks in his hands and can put my finger in them, and put my hand into the hole in his side, I will not believe.'

But I went back to Jerusalem with them. Even though I couldn't accept what they said, or feel what they felt, they were still my best friends.

It happened just under a week later. There we were, together as usual, when who should appear in the room but

Jesus. Just like that. No fanfare of trumpets. No warning. He just appeared among us, saying hello and looking so like himself that for a second it was as if he'd never been away. I almost gave him the sort of laid-back 'Oh-hi-there' type of greeting a guy who keeps his feet on the ground gives when friends show up.

And then my eyes travelled from his face – which looked exactly the same – to his hands, which didn't. And I gave a sort of strangled gasp.

He stepped towards me. 'Go on. Feel the nailprints, Thomas.' It was obvious he knew what I'd said. 'Put your fist into my side. Stop doubting and believe.'

Even as he spoke, a crashing wave of belief swept over me, throwing me down at his feet. For the first time I knew who he really was. Maybe I'd half-believed it before, but now I was totally sure. 'My Lord and my God!' I cried.

And this is where you come in. For as Jesus helped me up he said: 'You've believed because you've seen me, but happy are those who have not seen and yet have believed.' Get that? 'Those who have not seen' are the men, women, girls and boys – millions of them – who, like you, have lived in the 2,000 years since Jesus went to the place where he was going, i.e. heaven.

So I've got a fact for you. I want you to face it and watch the effect it has on your secret self. Does it make you shake your head, or shrug, or smile wistfully in an 'if only . . .' sort of way? Or is this the very best news you've ever heard?

Here goes: Jesus *is* alive!

Teaching point

Jesus rose from the dead.

Bible reading

John 20:24–31.

Application

This story is a dramatic monologue. Lead into it by asking the group to imagine Thomas' feelings as they listen to John 20:24–31. After the reading say: 'If Thomas were here today, I wonder what he would say.' This is the cue for someone dressed as Thomas to come in and perform the monologue.

The monologue contains its own application. Afterwards, allow a few moments of silence for the group to make their individual response. Then repeat the Victory Shout (see below) together.

Victory Shout

Leader: Jesus is the King of kings
Group: Jesus is the King of kings
Leader: He's the Lord of everything
Group: He's the Lord of everything
Leader: He has conquered death and sin
Group: He has conquered death and sin
Leader: So today we trust in him
Group: So today we trust in him
All: **Jesus!**

Songs

Come and praise the Lord our King (JP 34)
God's not dead, (No) (SOFK 43, JP 60)
He is Lord (JP 75)
Jesus Christ is alive today (JP 129)
Jesus Christ is risen today, Hallelujah! (JP 130)
Jesus is Lord! Creation's voice proclaims it (JP 137)
Low in the grave He lay (JP 159)
One day when heaven was filled with His praises (JP 187)

Saviour of the world, thank You for dying on the cross
   (JP 216)
This joyful Eastertide (JP 256)
Jesus, Prince and Saviour (JP 407)
Easter jubilation (SOFK 26)

16. Mansions in Heaven

Once upon a time, not so long ago, two angels flew to earth. They were called Gabriel and Bob. Gabriel flew down majestically and Bob, who was younger and didn't know much, bobbed along behind. They had come to earth on a special house-hunting mission. In other words, they were searching for houses – houses which deserved to be rebuilt in heaven at the end of the age.

The two angels landed with a swish and a plop on the outskirts of a big city.

There before them was a magnificent mansion, surrounded by a high security fence. It had thirty windows at the front and great oak doors. The name on the gate said: 'Buckington Palace'.

93

'Wow!' said Bob, really impressed. 'Come on, Gabe. This looks promising.'

So the angels flew up to the house, landing with a swish and a plop on the front balcony.

Gabriel took out his notebook (being the older angel, he was the one who made the decisions) and Bob got on with the interview.

'Good afternoon,' he began in a chatty manner. 'We're angels and we're doing a little door-to-door work. We've been asking all the houses in this area the same simple question. Can you think of any reason why you should be rebuilt in heaven when you crumble?'

There was a cold silence. Then the great house said in a very offended tone, 'I'll have you know that thousands of pounds are spent each year on my upkeep. I am in absolutely no danger of crumbling . . .'

'OK, keep your roof on, Buckington,' soothed Bob. 'Let's forget the crumbling bit. Just tell us why you should be rebuilt in heaven.'

'Well I'd have thought that was quite obvious,' sniffed the house. 'Just look at me! With seven reception rooms, four bathrooms, ten bedrooms and a swimming pool, I offer a very high standard of accommodation.'

Bob looked at Gabriel, who turned away with a slight shake of his noble head.

'So Buckington Palace hasn't made it into heaven, right?' said Bob as they flew on into the city.

'Right,' said Gabriel. 'You don't get into heaven because you look good.'

The next house the angels came to was a red-brick bungalow. It was nowhere near as impressive as Buckington Palace, but it had nice clean windows and a well-kept garden. 'This is Pinetree Cottage,' said Bob. 'Not bad, eh?' He pressed the doorbell and it chimed sweetly.

Gabriel took out his notebook and Bob got down to the interview.

'Good afternoon. We're angels and we're doing a little door-to-door work. We've been asking all the houses in this area the same simple question. Can you think of any reason why you should be rebuilt in heaven when you crumble?'

There was a shocked silence. The bungalow lowered its blinds, then slowly raised them back up again.

'I'd rather not talk about crumbling,' it murmured. 'What I think is private – like my garden.'

'Well let's not talk about crumbling, then,' nodded Bob. 'Just tell us why you should be rebuilt in heaven.'

'Because I've worked hard all my life,' the bungalow said. 'Because I've kept my windows clean and my paintwork fresh, and my hedges trimmed. Because I've gone regularly to the interior designer. Because I've had all sorts of home improvements. Because . . . well . . . because I've earned it.'

Bob looked over at Gabriel, who turned away sadly.

'So Pinetree Cottage hasn't made it into heaven either, right?' asked Bob as they flew on down the street.

'Right,' nodded Gabriel. 'No one can earn a place in heaven.'

The third house the angels came to was called 'The Traveller's Rest'. Some of its windows were cracked and it looked badly in need of a coat of paint. 'Bit of a flaky joint this,' shrugged Bob, as he lifted the knocker.

Despite its run-down appearance The Traveller's Rest was remarkably cheerful.

'Come in. Come in. I've been expecting you.' It flung open its doors and welcomed the angels inside. 'Up the stairs. First on the left. The beds are made up. Just go right in and make yourselves at home.'

The angels did as they were told – Gabriel climbing majestically with Bob bobbing along behind. They found themselves in a plain little bedroom with two beds, two easy chairs, a table and a cot.

'I'm sorry,' the house apologised. 'I know it's not much, but it was the best I could manage at short notice. In fact I had to ask some of my other guests to double up to squeeze you in. They were very understanding. Soon as they heard you were a homeless couple with a young baby, they were happy to help. . . .' There was a short pause. 'Where *is* the baby, by the way?'

'What baby?' said Bob. 'We never had a baby.'

'Oops there's been a mix-up! The church down the road told me to expect a homeless couple with a small baby,' cried the house. 'Then you arrive without the baby. Next you'll be telling me you aren't homeless.'

'We aren't,' said Bob. 'We're angels, and we're in these parts doing a little. . . .'

'Angels!' interrupted the house. 'Gosh! I'm sorry I didn't recognise you. I've become a bit short-sighted since my windows cracked. I'm expecting a homeless couple, you see, with a small baby. They've travelled a long way and they really will need a bit of peace and quiet. So if you don't mind. . . .'

'Not at all. It's been a pleasure to meet you. Come along, Bob.' To Bob's surprise Gabriel didn't even give him a chance to do his interview. He simply grabbed him by the wing and swept him back down the stairs. To his even greater surprise he could see that the majestic angel was beaming from ear to ear.

'Well, we've found what we're looking for, Bob,' he said.

'Have we?' replied Bob, scratching his head.

The archangel put a hand on his young companion's shoulder. 'Ask yourself what kind of a house that was.'

Bob scratched his head again. 'Ummm . . . it opened its doors . . . it welcomed strangers . . . well, you could say it was a loving kind of house, I suppose.'

'You could indeed,' beamed Gabriel. 'Which means it belongs to the King of Love – which means it has a place in heaven with him at the end of the age.'

Teaching point

Jesus gives eternal life to those who belong to him.

Bible reading

John 14:1–6.

Application

After telling the story ask the group who Gabriel meant when he talked about the King of Love (Jesus). Show a picture of Jesus talking to his disciples and lead into the Bible reading by saying that while he was on earth Jesus taught his followers about many things and that this is what he had to say about getting into heaven. Then read John 14:1–6. Finish by teaching the action rhyme below.

Action rhyme

You don't get to heaven by looking like a star   *(pose as model)*
You don't get to heaven by strength and earning power
   (flex muscles)
You don't get to heaven by hoping that you may
   (fingers crossed)
You get there by trusting Jesus . . .   *(point upwards)*
He's the only way.   *(move hands forward to show a path)*

Songs

Do you want a Pilot (JP 40)
I am the Way, the Truth and the Life (JP 89)

Jesus, I will come with You (JP 138)
Jesus loves me this I know (JP 140)
The Lord's my Shepherd (SOFK 162)
I am the Resurrection and the Life (JP 368)

MAY

Party-Time

17. S.O.S.

(A true story from Germany)

Can you imagine what a tight squeeze it would be sharing an ordinary-sized house with twenty-six other people? That was the amount of space a group of twenty-six German women had when God first led them to live together as a family. Then one bright May morning God told them to build a special centre in his honour.

At the time it seemed impossible. The Mary Sisters (as they were called) had no land or money, and getting official permission for building usually took years. But eighteen months after they started their building project, the walls of their new home were up and the foundations of a church were ready to be laid.

So much had happened so quickly that, even though there

wasn't a proper roof on their new home yet, the sisters decided to throw a party. They set a date and invited lots of people, including the architect and the city building superintendent, the masons and the truck-drivers, the government officials and the building suppliers. The plan was to hold the celebration in the covered basement area of the building. It would be a way of saying 'thank you' to their human helpers. But most of all it would be a way of saying 'thank you' to God.

Then, the night before the party, a terrible storm blew up. The sisters, huddled on their mattresses, had never seen anything like it. It was the storm to end all storms. The wind howled. The lightning flashed. You'd have thought there was a burst pipe in heaven the rain came down so hard.

By morning the wind had dropped, but the rain was still pouring down. 'Let's hope it clears up soon,' the sisters said to each other as they squelched across the muddy building site with all the things they needed for the party that afternoon.

They made their way down to the basement.

Drip . . . drip . . . drip. That was the sound that greeted them as they entered the room. Plop! A drop of water landed on their leader's head. Plop! She felt another. And another.

The basement ceiling was leaking – and not just in one or two places. The sisters' hearts sank as they realised the size of the problem. Every brick in the ceiling was water-logged and dripping like a sponge. And there was no other room in which they could entertain their guests. What was to be done? Even if the rain stopped immediately, the dripping would go on, and the builders, the truck-drivers and all those important government officials would end up soaked to the skin.

It was too late to cancel the invitations. So the sisters did the only thing they could. They prayed. They prayed as they spread the white linen cloths on the tables. They prayed as they laid out the cups (turning each one upside-down on its saucer to keep out the drips). They prayed as they put up umbrellas over the cakes.

And as they prayed, they remembered how, 2,000 years earlier, another party had hit problems. Not the problem of guests about to be dripped on, but the problem of guests having nothing to drink. Like the Mary Sisters, the organisers of that party were facing a disaster – until Jesus stepped in and changed six large jars of water into six jars of the finest wine.

He had come to the rescue at that party. Would he come to the rescue at their party too?

The Mary Sisters were praying for a miracle.

And, when they showed their guests into that basement room a few hours later, a miracle was what they got.

The guests stayed dry. In the other rooms on the basement level, water continued to drip down steadily for the rest of the day. But in the room where the tables were laid out for tea the dripping stopped. Throughout the celebrations, not a single drop of water landed on the tables or the decorations or on a single guest's head.

Of course the guests didn't notice they weren't being dripped on. What they *did* notice, though, was God's presence and power. Everyone felt it – every builder, every truck-driver, every government official. God poured out his love in the basement that afternoon.

And *that* – as the sisters said afterwards – was the best miracle of all.

Teaching point

Emergency prayer.

Bible reading

John 2:1–10.

Application

Before telling the story read John 2:1–10. Afterwards hold up a sign saying 'S.O.S.' and explain that until recently this was the international distress signal, the letters standing for Save Our Souls. Point out that the letters could also stand for Seeking, Obedient and Sure. The Mary Sisters were all of those things. They were *Seeking* God's will. They were *Obedient* to his word. And they were *Sure* of his love. When adults and children who are seeking, obedient and sure hit an emergency, they send up an S.O.S. prayer. God may not always work a miracle, but one way or another he will always answer that call.

Extra information

The Evangelical Sisterhood of Mary is based in Hesse Darmstadt. The source of this story is *Realities: The Miracles of God Experienced Today* by Basilea Schlink (Zondervan, 1966).

Songs

Come to Jesus, 'He's amazing' (JP 33)
Father I place into Your hands (SOFK 28, JP 42)
I am trusting You, Lord Jesus (JP 86)
I do not know what lies ahead (JP 92)
My God is so big, so strong and so mighty (SOFK 134, JP 169)
Peter and James and John in a sailboat (JP 197)
Mighty is our God (JP 431)
Oh no! The wine's all gone (JP 437)

18. Wedding Guests

King Peter, the ruler of Paradise Island, had made up his mind to get married. 'I'm off to search the world for a bride,' he told his advisers. So off he went, and for the next few years the islanders kept getting postcards from all the different places he visited. Then, one day, a ship docked in the harbour and the Royal Herald raced ashore with the news everyone had been waiting for.

'King Peter has found his bride and he's on his way home!' the Herald announced. 'Invitations to his wedding feast can be picked up from outside the Royal Palace tomorrow morning.'

Naturally *everyone* wanted to go to the feast. But two islanders were especially glad about the wedding. They were

Dophne, the island dressmaker, and her husband, Fronk. (Their real names were Daphne and Frank, but they called themselves Fronk and Dophne because it sounded posher.) They were especially glad because they expected to earn loads of money making wedding outfits for all the islanders.

But the couple were in for a disappointment.

As they joined the queue to pick up their invitations the following day, they saw people walking away from the palace with linen tunics.

'What are the tunics for?' Dophne asked two women as they passed.

'They're wedding garments,' the women replied.

Wedding garments!!

By this stage Fronk and Dophne had reached the top of the queue and, sure enough, they were given wedding garments too. 'King Peter has sent each of his guests a linen tunic to wear to his wedding,' the Herald explained.

The first thing Fronk and Dophne did when they got home was toss their white tunics into the bin.

'It isn't fair. This wedding should have been the fashion event of the year!' Dophne moaned.

Fronk looked thoughtful. 'Listen, Dophne. I'm sure some of the other islanders won't like this any more than we do. So let's give them a choice. Let's make up some wedding tunics of our own so that they won't have to wear King Peter's tunics after all.'

'Fronk, you're a genius! That's a brilliant idea,' said Dophne as she grabbed a notebook and started sketching. 'We'll make our own exclusive range of wedding garments. We'll have nylon tunics with fluffy white rabbits for children ... and satin tunics with pearl buttons for ladies ... and silk tunics with bow ties for men. ...'

The idea worked like a dream. Some people bought Fronk and Dophne's tunics straight away. Others began by saying they would wear King Peter's tunics and then changed their mind because they wanted to be as well dressed as their neighbours. One way or another, in a matter of months, the couple had persuaded several hundred islanders to make the switch.

At then, at long last, King Peter returned to the island with his lovely bride.

The wedding day had come, and Fronk and Dophne were feeling extremely pleased with themselves.

'My darling, you look spectacular,' said Fronk when he saw his wife, dressed for the party, in her hand-embroidered, crushed satin, off-the-shoulder wedding garment with matching gloves.

'My angel, so do you,' cried Dophne, admiring the perfect cut of her husband's glittering tunic and tie. 'We must make sure we arrive at the palace a little late so that all the other guests get a good look at us as we come in.'

As planned, the dressmaker and her husband were the very last guests to reach the palace gates. There was just one family in front of them – a man and woman and their three children, all wearing plain white tunics. Fronk and Dophne looked at them scornfully. 'Imagine turning up for a Royal Wedding dressed like that,' they said to each other. 'They look so shabby compared to us.'

But a very strange thing happened as the little family handed their invitations to the gate-keeper. The moment they stepped through the gates their simple tunics started to sparkle. Suddenly, instead of looking shabby, they seemed to be clothed in purest gold.

'It must be a trick of the light,' Fronk whispered to Dophne as they watched the family disappear through the wide open palace doors.

It was their turn to hand in their invitations.

The gate-keeper was a keen-eyed old man with a long grey beard. He looked Fronk and Dophne up and down and shrugged. 'You can go on through the gates if you like, but you won't stay long,' he muttered.

'Of *course* we'll stay!' Dophne assured him. 'We want *everyone* to see us . . . I mean,' she corrected herself quickly, 'we want to see everyone.'

'Silly old fellow,' she added under her breath, as she and Fronk swept in through the gates.

The couple made it as far as the entrance hall. They came close enough to hear the music, to glimpse the magnificent wedding cake and smell the delicious food. And then they caught sight of two tramps. One was wearing a dirty, tattered, off-the-shoulder wedding garment, and the other was wearing an even dirtier, more tattered, silk tunic and tie. 'Oh, look at that pair!' Dophne wrinkled her nose in disgust. And immediately the tramp in the off-the-shoulder garment wrinkled her nose too. What?!

Suddenly the penny dropped. The tramps were *them*. They were looking at themselves in a full-length mirror. 'Dophne, our wedding garments have turned into rags,' gasped Fronk. 'Come on. Let's get out of here!'

So Fronk and Dophne took to their heels and ran home as fast as they could – only to discover that they hadn't just ruined their own chances of being guests at the wedding, they had spoiled things for hundreds of other islanders as well. There was an angry crowd waiting outside their workshop. 'Those tunics you made us turned into rags the minute we went through the palace gates,' they were shouting. 'We're missing the Royal Wedding and it's all thanks to you.'

Shame-faced, Fronk and Dophne slipped into the house through the back door. And that night, while King Peter and his bride and their guests made merry in the palace, they slipped out with a suitcase and went down to the harbour. There they got into a boat and sailed away. And no one has ever seen or heard of them since.

Teaching point

God wants to clothe us in the Spirit of Christ.

Bible reading

Matthew 22:11–14.

Application

After telling the story say that it is a sort of parable and find out if the group know what a parable is (a story with a hidden meaning). Say that the clue to the hidden meaning to the story is in Matthew 22:11–14. Read it, then ask the group which of the following sentences they think best sums up the hidden meaning:

1. To be guests at God's party in heaven we need to dress well on earth.
2. To be guests at God's party in heaven we all need to wear the same clothes.
3. To be guests at God's party in heaven we need to be clothed in the Spirit of Christ.

Briefly elaborate on the correct answer, with reference to the words of the action song below. Finish by singing the song together.

Action song *(to the tune of 'Give me oil in my lamp')*

I've been asked to a party in heaven
And King Jesus will be there.
He's sent me my own invitation
And it tells me what the guests should wear.

Sing Hosanna, sing Hosanna, sing Hosanna to the King of kings.
Sing Hosanna, sing Hosanna, sing Hosanna to the King.

Sin has made my old clothes look so dirty
I've decided to throw them out.
I can't wear dirty clothes to a party,
Where everything is fresh and bright.

chorus

God has giv'n me a beautiful garment;
It's shining, it's soft, it's clean.
For it's made of the pure love of Jesus
And wearing it, I look like him.

chorus

(v.1 – group mime opening invitation; v.2 – mime throwing away old clothes; v.3 – mime putting on new clothes)

Songs

He brought me to His banqueting house (JP 73)
Jesus, how lovely You are (SOFK 107, JP 133)
Jesus is a friend of mine (JP 136)
Surely goodness and mercy shall follow me (JP 223)
The Lord's my Shepherd (SOFK 162)
Come on and celebrate! (SOFK 15, JP 325)
Sing and celebrate (JP 457)

19. *Measured, Measured, Weighed, Divided*

The time is midnight. The place is Babylon. And in the banqueting hall in the Royal Palace there's a romping, stomping, hooting, shouting party going on.*

There sits King Belshazzar, surrounded by his wives, his girlfriends and one thousand of his noblemen. He has tons to eat and gallons to drink. But he looks fed up.

'Come on, loosen up, everyone!' he orders.

His thousand noble guests do their best.* But Belshazzar still feels bored.

Then suddenly he has a brainwave.

'Fetch the golden goblets that were taken from the Temple in Jerusalem,' he orders his servants. 'Fill them with wine and pass them round. Tell my noble guests that the cups they are drinking from belong to the One True God.'

Next thing Belshazzar has started to enjoy himself. It's fun making fun of the One True God.

A moment later he has another bright idea. He decides to use the temple goblets to drink toasts to other gods!

'A toast to the god of gold!'*

'A toast to the god of silver!'*

'A toast to the god of wood!'*

'A toast to the god of stone!'*

After every toast his nobles raise the roof – romping, stomping, hooting and shouting for all they are worth.*

And then, at the height of the merry-making, all the romping, stomping, hooting and shouting suddenly stops. Something happens. Something really weird. A ghostly hand appears out of nowhere and starts writing on the wall. Gasp! The women clap their hands to their mouths. Gulp! The noblemen's jaws drop. Knock . . . knock . . . knockity . . . knock! King Belshazzar's smile fades and his knees start knocking in fear.

For minutes that seem like hours the hand writes; then, as quietly as it appeared, it vanishes, leaving four words written on the wall: 'measured, measured, weighed, divided'.

No one is in any doubt that it's a message from the One True God. The question is: What does it mean?

Panic-stricken, Belshazzar sends for his astrologers and magicians. For minutes that seem like hours they study the writing on the wall. They get into a huddle and talk about the meaning. But in the end they have to admit they haven't a clue.

At this point the queen mother sweeps into the banqueting hall.

'Just look at that wall!' wails Belshazzar. 'We were just having a bit of fun when a ghostly hand appeared and wrote those words. And nobody can tell me what they mean. And the whole creepy business is driving me mad.'

'Calm down,' says the queen mother. 'I know someone who can help. He's a man called Daniel – a servant of the One True God.'

'Send for him,' Belshazzar says, pouring himself another drink. 'If he can really help I'll give him a purple robe and make him the third highest ruler in the land.'

And so Daniel is summoned to the Royal Palace.

'You see my problem,' says Belshazzar, waving towards the writing on the wall. 'I need to know what that message means. I'll give you a purple robe and make you the third highest ruler in the land if you can tell me.'

'I'll tell you what the writing means,' says Daniel. 'But you can keep your gifts. I know what you've been up to. You've had no respect for the One True God. You've been drinking from the temple goblets and praising gods of wood and stone.'

Belshazzar shrugs – an I-didn't-bring-you-here-to-give-me-a-lecture sort of shrug. Solemnly Daniel turns back to the four words on the wall and reads them aloud.

'Belshazzar, this is what these words mean,' he says. 'The length or "measure" of your days as King has come to an end. Your character has been tested or "weighed" by God, and you have failed. Your kingdom will be "divided" between your enemies.'

A gasp of horror goes round the banqueting hall.

But to everyone's amazement Belshazzar simply yawns. Now he knows what the message means, all he wants to do is stumble off to bed. 'Tomorrow is another day,' he yawns. 'With any luck I'll wake up to discover this "measured, weighed, divided" business is all a bad dream.'

But it isn't and he doesn't.

For that night his Persian enemies launch a surprise attack. And before the party dishes are even cleared from the tables, everything happens exactly as Daniel said it would. The Persian army triumphs. Babylon is divided. And

Belshazzar's romping, stomping, hooting, shouting reign is at an end.*

Teaching point

The importance of not letting fun times get out of hand.

Bible passage

This story is based on Daniel 5:1–31.

Telling the story

Give a party hooter to each member of the group before-hand and tell them they are to hoot loudly each time you raise your hand and when you lower your hand they must stop (on peril of losing their hooter). Tell the story, cuing in hoots as indicated by an asterisk in the text. If the group is a large one, give out a number of hooters and get everyone else to make other party sounds, e.g. clapping, stamping and shouting.

NB Only do this if you are confident that the fun won't get out of hand!

Application

Begin by asking the group to imagine a group of vandals had stolen all the Bibles from the church and burned them on a huge bonfire. Then introduce the story by saying that in 539 BC something a little bit like that happened to some sacred goblets which the Jews had kept in the Temple in Jerusalem. After telling the story display pictures of King Belshazzar, the noblemen and Daniel and ask the group how they would describe their behaviour at the party. Aim to bring out the fact that Belshazzar was *Looking for a thrill*, the noblemen were *Going with the crowd* and Daniel was *In touch with God*. How do we behave in party situations? Point out that keeping in touch with God doesn't mean we can't have fun. It just means we won't go along with the crowd if the fun gets out of hand.

Songs

Daniel was a man of prayer (JP 36)
He brought me to His banqueting house (JP 73)
I met Jesus at the crossroads (JP 102)
In our work and in our play (JP 108)
My Lord is higher than a mountain (JP 170)
Be holy in all that you do (JP 314)
Lord, You are brilliant, champion of champions (JP 423)
There once was a man called Daniel (JP 477)

20. *Sir Grumpy and the Parrot*

(Pentecost)

A gloomy knight once lived all alone at the top of a high tower. He was called Sir Grumpy, because he grumbled about everything – his home, his friends, his job, the weather. He even grumbled about his birthday.

Our story begins at nine o'clock on the morning of Sir Grumpy's fortieth birthday when the postman came with a parcel and left it outside his front door. Now most people would be delighted to receive a parcel in the post. But Sir Grumpy wasn't delighted – not when he had to march all the way down ninety-six steps to collect it.

'Oh bother! Parcels are such a nuisance,' he grumbled.

The parcel was a birthday present. 'To my dearest Grumpy, from your loving Auntie Marigold,' the label read. Grumbling away, Sir Grumpy began to open the box.

'It'll be socks as usual,' he grumbled. 'I hate socks.'

But to Sir Grumpy's great surprise, when he lifted the lid a brilliant green, blue and yellow parrot flew out. To his even greater surprise, this beautiful bird seemed to like the way he looked. Black eyes twinkling, it peered up into his face. 'Hiya, Gorgeous,' it squawked.

Shocked, Sir Grumpy pulled his helmet down over his ears.

When he lifted the visor back up, the parrot was still staring at him with delight. 'My hero!' it trilled.

This was the first time Sir Grumpy had ever been called a hero and it gave him a nice warm feeling inside. Marching back up the ninety-six stairs with his present, he decided to write and thank Auntie Marigold for sending him such a clever bird. Then he decided to call his pet Polly. By the time he'd reached his room, he'd made up his mind to throw a party so that all his friends could hear what Polly said.

Sir Grumpy only had two friends – Sir Happy and Sir Helpful – and they were a very jolly pair. 'A party! Excellent idea, Old Boy. We'd *love* to come,' they agreed. The trouble was, once they got there things didn't work out the way Sir Grumpy had planned. His idea was that Sir Happy and Sir Helpful would sit around the tea table listening to Polly saying nice things about him – Sir Grumpy. But instead, Sir Happy and Sir Helpful started making a fuss of Polly, which meant that Polly started to say nice things about them. This made Sir Grumpy crosser and crosser, until in the end he completely lost his temper. 'Leave her alone. She's mine!' he shouted, and he snatched their plates away.

'I say, Old Boy. Hang on a minute. We haven't tasted your birthday cake yet,' cried Sir Happy.

'I'm not sharing my cake with anyone but Polly,' said Sir Grumpy. 'The party's over. Go home.'

Well, there was nothing else for it. Sir Happy and Sir Helpful had to go. The minute they were out of the way Sir Grumpy lit the forty candles on his cake. He took a deep breath and blew them all out in one blow. 'Time for my wish,' he told Polly. He shut his eyes and he said: 'I wish to keep Polly all to myself from now on.'

Next morning Sir Grumpy decided to make his wish come true. He marched off into town, went to the department store and spent all his birthday money on a golden cage, so splendid it even had a velvet carpet and a parrot-sized swimming pool. He brought the cage home and put Polly inside. Then he stood back and waited. 'Go on, say it. Say thank you, Grumpy,' he smiled. But even though the cage was so luxurious and had cost a small fortune, Polly didn't say a word.

She didn't speak the next day either – or the next day – or the next.

By the end of the week Sir Grumpy was so fed up with Polly not talking, he marched off to Auntie Marigold's to complain.

He found his little old aunt sitting peacefully by the fire with her knitting.

'That parrot you gave me won't talk,' Sir Grumpy grumbled. 'What's more, she's stopped eating. She just lies at the bottom of the cage.'

When Auntie Marigold heard the word 'cage', she seemed to swell up to twice her usual size. She grabbed her knitting bag and started pelting her nephew with balls of wool. 'You silly, selfish excuse for a knight,' she raged. Then she hobbled outside, hopped onto her bicycle and pedalled off down the road.

She was there at the top of the ninety-six steps when Sir Grumpy got back to his tower – there to take Polly away. 'You don't deserve a beautiful parrot,' she scolded. 'Let alone an affectionate aunt.'

From the tower window Sir Grumpy watched them go –
Auntie Marigold riding her bike, with Polly flying along
behind. 'Good riddance,' he muttered. But he didn't mean it.
The truth was, deep down he was feeling really miserable.
And the further away Polly flew, the more miserable he felt.
Suddenly he could bear it no longer. He flung open the tower
window. 'Come back, Polly,' he shouted at the top of his
voice. 'I'll do *anything* . . . anything at all . . . to put things
right.'

No sooner were the words out of his mouth than a
wonderful thing happened. Polly did a somersault in mid-air
and started flying back towards the tower.

'I'll do anything,' Sir Grumpy kept shouting. 'I'll wash
behind my ears . . . I'll keep my bedroom tidy . . . I'll run up
and down the stairs a hundred times a day. . . .'

By this stage Polly had reached the window.

'Bye bye cage. Bye bye cage,' she squawked.

Of course! The cage! Why hadn't he thought of it sooner?
Immediately Sir Grumpy grabbed the golden cage and
hurled it – bumpity, bumpity, bump – down the stairs.

And as the cage went out, Polly came in. Hurrah! Sir
Grumpy was jumping for joy. 'Oh Polly,' he cried. 'Things
will be different from now on.'

And they were. From that day on Sir Grumpy stopped
grumbling. He let Polly fly where she pleased. He shared her
with his friends, and patched things up with Auntie
Marigold. And before long he became known as Sir
Gracious, because he had turned into one of the kindest,
friendliest, cheeriest knights in town.

Teaching point

The Holy Spirit is God's birthday gift to the church. Are we
letting the Spirit move freely in our hearts and lives?

Bible readings

Acts 2:1–4; 1 Thessalonians 5:19.

Application

Before telling the story read Acts 2:1–4 and explain that the Holy Spirit was God's birthday gift to the church. Then tell the story using illustrations, including a gift-wrapped box and a cage.

After telling the story, refer back to these illustrations. Hold up the gift illustration and ask: What was the wonderful birthday gift God gave his people on the Day of Pentecost? (The Holy Spirit.) Then hold up the cage and remind the group that in the story Sir Grumpy made the mistake of trying to keep his gift shut up in a cage. Explain that we can make the same mistake sometimes, when we try to keep the Holy Spirit shut up in one little part of our lives. Finish by teaching the action rhyme below, which encourages the group not to do this.

Action rhyme *(can be sung to the tune of 'Earth rejoice our Lord is King' or 'Father lead me day by day')*

Let the Holy Spirit move, (*hands held up*)
Let him fill our hearts with love. (*hands on heart*)
Every hour of every day, (*turn round in a circle – to represent earth moving*)
Let God's Spirit have his way. (*hands held up again*)

Songs

All over the world the Spirit is moving (JP 5)
God whose Son was once a man on earth (JP 62)
I want to walk with Jesus Christ (SOFK 100, JP 124)

Love, joy, peace and patience, kindness (JP 158)
Spirit of the living God, fall afresh on me (JP 222)
Jesus, send me the helper (JP 409)
Spirit of God please fill me now to overflowing (JP 465)
The Spirit lives to set us free (JP 472)

JUNE

Before and After

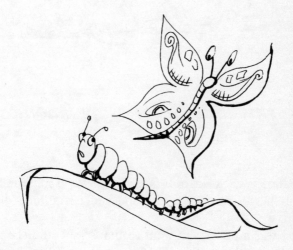

21. Amy and the Missing Gnomes

Mrs Clark was a school caretaker. She lived beside the school she took care of, and she had ten gnomes in her garden.

Amy was a pupil who went to the school, and she really liked naming things. She called her bicycle 'Wheels' and her schoolbag 'Carrie'. She called her church 'the Crosspatch' (because there was a poster with a cross on it in the patch of grass outside) and her school 'the Chalkface'; and she had a name for each of Mrs Clark's gnomes. Happy, Dopey, Grumpy, Sleepy, Tidy, Smiley, Tiny, Chatty and Messy was what she called them – and then there was the big gnome with twinkling eyes and a bristling black beard which she had christened Mr Babbington, after her headmaster.

One day, during the summer holidays, when the Chalkface was locked up and Mrs Clark was away in her caravan at the seaside, it so happened that Amy was passing the caretaker's cottage with her best friend, Laurin, and she decided to show off a little.

'See those gnomes. I've got names for them all,' she said.

'OK. Let's hear them.'

So Amy reeled them off: 'Happy, Dopey, Grumpy, Sleepy, Tidy, Smiley, Tiny. . . .' Suddenly she stopped. 'Oh no!' She clapped her hand to her mouth. 'One's gone missing. Chatty's disappeared.'

'Ha! Ha! Maybe Mrs Clark took him off to the caravan with her,' giggled Laurin.

'Don't be silly,' said Amy.

'Well, what do you think has happened to him then?' Laurin asked.

'I don't know,' Amy frowned. 'Perhaps he's been stolen.'

She didn't sleep very well that night puzzling over the mystery. First thing next morning she cycled back to Mrs Clark's gate to see if the missing gnome had returned. But there was no sign of it. Worse still, a second gnome, Tidy, had gone too.

Now Amy knew there was definitely something funny going on – something she would have to put a stop to.

So she hopped over the wall into the garden, and hid in a rose-bed. She stayed there for the next three hours. It was a very prickly, boring sort of way to pass the morning, but Amy was determined that if thieves came back and tried to steal another gnome, she would be there to leap out and stop them.

And then, just as she was about to give up and go home for lunch, another gnome *did* disappear. And this time Amy was there to see how it went. Before her eyes a tall, bearded man walked into the garden, picked up a gnome and stuffed it into his briefcase. But the really amazing thing was she recognised the thief. It was Mr Babbington, her head-master.

And that was where Amy's plan came unstuck. Somehow she couldn't bring herself to leap out of the roses on top of her headmaster shouting: 'Stop thief!' So she stayed where she was until Mr Babbington was safely out of sight.

Then on her way home, she called in at the Crosspatch where Elaine, her Sunday school teacher, ran a play-group every morning.

'What would you do if you saw someone stealing things?' she asked Elaine.

Elaine thought for a moment. 'That would depend,' she said. 'What sort of things are we talking about?'

'Well, school things – sort of,' said Amy.

'Ah, in that case I would report it to your headmaster,' said Elaine.

'But what if the thief *is* the headmaster?' cried Amy. 'You see I've just seen Mr Babbington stealing the gnomes out of Mrs Clark's garden. He's taken three so far. And I don't know what to do. Do you think I should report him to the police?'

Elaine didn't think this was a good idea.

'Look, why don't you leave this with me,' she said. 'I'll go round to the school and check things out.'

For the second night in a row, Amy didn't sleep well. She kept waking up and wondering whether Mr Babbington was out there stealing more gnomes, and whether Elaine really would be able to stop him.

Not long after breakfast the doorbell rang. Drrrrring. Amy raced to answer it, only to find Elaine on the doorstep.

'You've to come along to the school with me, Amy,' Elaine said. 'Mr Babbington wants to speak to you.'

'Arrgh! Help! What's he going to say?' said Amy in a panic. But there was nothing else for it. To the school she had to go.

Shaking in her shoes, the girl stood waiting outside the headmaster's study.

Finally the door opened and Mr Babbington strode out. 'Follow me,' he said gruffly.

So Amy followed him; round a corner, down a corridor, up a flight of stairs, down another corridor and into the art room – where a wonderful sight met her eyes. She saw three gleaming gnomes, freshly painted in all the colours of the rainbow.

'Ahem.' Mr Babbington cleared his throat. 'As you can see, Amy, I haven't been stealing. I just wanted to brighten up as many of Mrs Clark's garden ornaments as possible while she was away. You might say that painting gnomes has been my secret holiday hobby.'

So that was it. Mr Babbington had been painting the gnomes, not stealing them. Amy was very relieved.

'You know something, Sir?' she said. 'This whole mix-up reminds me of God.'

'Does it?' the headmaster asked, looking at her in amazement.

'Yes,' Amy nodded. 'I used to be mixed-up about him too. I used to think he was out to steal the fun from people's lives. But then I discovered all he wanted was to make my life a whole lot brighter and better – just like you did to the garden gnomes. Of course,' she added quickly, 'I don't mean God's going round with a giant paintbrush. I'm thinking about Jesus. . . .'

'I know you are, Amy,' the headmaster smiled. 'And it's a very good thought – a very good thought indeed.'

Teaching point

The difference Jesus makes.

Bible reading

John 10:7–10.

Application

Hold up the two words BEFORE and AFTER and say that the group have just heard a 'Before and After' story. There was a Before and After for the gnomes: *before* Mr Babbington painted them they were dull, and *after* he painted them they were bright; and there was a Before and After for Amy: *before* she went into the art room she thought her headmaster was a thief, and *after* she went in she realised he wasn't. Then say that there was one other Before and After in the story. Can anyone think what it was? (Amy said that *before* she understood about Jesus she thought God was out to steal the fun from people's lives, but *after* she understood, she saw God just wanted to make her life brighter and better.)

Introduce the Bible passage as a reading which talks about this new brighter, better abundant life that Jesus can give us. Read John 10:7–10. Finish by teaching the action song below.

Action song *(can be sung to the tune of 'Ten Green Bottles')*

The thief comes to steal from us,   *(mime taking something)*
Jesus gives new life.   *(mime giving something)*
The thief takes our money,   *(mime empty pockets or purse)*
Jesus keeps us safe.   *(clasp one hand in the other)*
To trust a thief is crazy,   *(thumbs down)*
He tells a pack of lies;   *(shout 'rubbish')*
But Jesus truly loves us,   *(thumbs up)*
So trusting him is wise.   *(shout 'Jesus')*

Songs

Come let us sing of a wonderful love (JP 29)
Come on, let's get up and go (SOFK 16, JP 31)

'Follow me' says Jesus (JP 46)
Happiness is to know the Saviour (JP 70)
If you want joy, real joy, wonderful joy (JP 96)
I serve a risen Saviour (JP 113)
I've got that joy, joy, joy, joy (JP 121)
Live, live, live (JP 153)
There's new life in Jesus, lift up your heart (JP 249)
Who put the colours in the rainbow? (SOFK 191, JP 288)

22. Like Father, Like Son

(A true story for Father's Day)

This is a true story about four people.

It's about a missionary nurse called Katie MacKinnon.

It's about a baby boy called Kipngeno (pronounced Kim-yay-no).

It's about a villager called arap Rob, whose wife had just died.

And it's about an African chief called Chief arap Sang.

Now sometimes when people hear the words 'African Chief' they can get the wrong idea. Chief arap Sang wasn't the old-fashioned sort of chief who lived in a mud hut. He was a well-educated government official. He lived in a solid brick bungalow, and he went to the office each morning dressed in a smart suit.

One day, on the way to his office, Chief arap Sang heard something that puzzled him. (This was what made him so good at his job. He might have known all about twentieth-century medicine and science, but he also kept his ear to the ground and knew what was really going on in people's lives.) It was something about the villager arap Rob. Apparently arap Rob was going around saying that one of the children the nurse Katie MacKinnon was caring for was his baby son, and Chief arap Sang felt sure this couldn't be true. According to his information, arap Rob's son had been cursed by a witch-doctor – which could only mean one thing: arap Rob's baby was dead.

There was something fishy here, the chief decided – something he would have to look in to. So he sent a message to the hospital asking Katie to come and see him.

When Katie got the chief's message her legs turned to jelly. She knew how important the chief was, and she couldn't think of any good reason why he should want to meet her. Had someone complained about her work? she wondered nervously. Was she about to be expelled from the country?

But it was nothing like that. The chief just wanted to get to the bottom of the mystery.

'As you can see there is no one else in this room with us,' he told Katie when she arrived at his office. 'You can tell me the truth and you need not be afraid of me. I want to know whose baby you have in your house. You have been saying it is the son of a man called arap Rob. But *I* know that arap Rob's baby could not live because it was cursed. This means that you must be looking after another baby for arap Rob, which is very kind of you. But just in case there are problems later on, you'd better tell me the name of the real father.'

Suddenly Katie started smiling. She had just seen what the chief was getting at, and she knew he was in for a surprise. 'The baby in my house is truly arap Rob's son,' she insisted.

'But that's impossible,' Chief arap Sang frowned. 'Arap Rob's baby was cursed.'

'That's true,' nodded Katie. (Here in the West we find the idea of people dying as the result of a curse very strange, but she had been away from home long enough to discover that curses could have a terrible effect.) 'Arap Rob's baby *was* cursed. He became sick and almost died. But, you know, there is a power greater than the power of the witch-doctors. The Lord Jesus healed that baby and he is now well and strong and growing bigger every day.'

Chief arap Sang shook his head. He was not a Christian, and to him this sounded most unlikely. He had been hoping to be able to settle the matter quietly in his office, but now he saw he would have to travel to the hospital and sort things out there.

So, a short time later, Katie found herself welcoming this very important official into her home. Once again her legs felt like jelly. She loved entertaining, but she knew this wasn't a social call.

'Oh Lord, please help the chief see that I'm telling the truth,' she prayed, as she led the way into the nursery. 'Help him to understand that your power is greater than the power of the witch-doctors. Help him to accept that Kipngeno really is arap Rob's child.'

They went through the door into a room full of cots. And there, playing happily, was baby Kipngeno.

For a moment Chief arap Sang studied the bright-eyed little boy. Then, beaming, he turned back to Katie. Even before he opened his mouth she could tell he now believed her.

'You are right,' he said. 'This is certainly arap Rob's boy.'

Praise God! Katie's prayers had been answered – but can you work out how?

Here's the answer: the chief had spotted the family resemblance. From the width of his forehead to the set of his chin, baby Kipngeno was the image of his dad.

Teaching point

Whether or not we look like our human fathers, as Christians we are called to be like our Father God.

Bible reading

1 Peter 1:14–15.

Application

Before telling the story, ask the children how they have celebrated or plan to celebrate Father's Day. Then produce a home-made Father's Day card. Show them the front cover and say that you will read what is inside after the story. After telling the story open the card and read out the rhyme (below). People may not know who our human fathers are the minute they look at us, but our words and actions should tell them about our special relationship with God. Finish by repeating or singing the action rhyme together.

Action rhyme *(can be sung to the tune of 'God has given us a book full of stories')*

There are fathers of all shapes and sizes (*draw figure in the air*)
Some are tall, some are broad, some are thin. (*use hands to indicate size*)
But God is our heavenly Father (*point upwards*)
And we should be holy, like him. (*hands together in prayer*)

(The word 'holy' may be explained in terms of loving the things that God loves, and hating the things he hates – something which we learn to do as we spend time talking to him.)

Extra information

Influenced by his contact with Christians, Chief arap Sang was converted to Christ. Today Peter Kipngeno is a young man of faith, and Katie MacKinnon continues to serve God in Kenya. The source of this story is *Love Breaks Through* by Katie MacKinnon (Christian Focus Publications, 1992).

Songs

Abba, Father (SOFK 1, JP 2)

Behold, what manner of love the Father has given unto us (SOFK 7, JP 15)

Father, I place into Your hands (SOFK 28, JP 42)

My God is so big, so strong and so mighty (SOFK 134, JP 169)

Be careful little hands what you do (JP 312)

Be holy in all that you do (JP 314)

Father God I wonder (SOFK 27, JP 337)

You are holy, so You hate all we do wrong (JP 500)

23. Catchem

(A true story from the eighteenth century)

At one time the village of Ettingshall in England was a very wicked place. It was the home of highwaymen, murderers and pickpockets. It was so dangerous that the lane linking it to the main road was known as 'Hell's Lane', and even the local police stayed away.

One of the people who lived in the village was a thief called Catchem. During the day Catchem used to hide among the trees at the bottom of Hell's Lane. Then when unsuspecting foot travellers came along the main road, he would leap out and catch 'em (that was how he got his name!).

'Your money or your life!' he would shout, ramming his weapon into their backs. And immediately his terrified victims would take out their purses, strip off their watches and jewellery, and throw them down on the ground.

One day, as Catchem lay in wait in his hiding-place, he heard the sound of hoof beats. Knowing the bad reputation of the area, travellers would usually speed up as they passed Hell's Lane, but, to the thief's surprise, these two riders slowed down and came to a halt. Next thing he heard them talking to each other.

'We'll stop here,' said the first.

'Yes it's an ideal spot,' the second agreed.

An ideal spot! Catchem almost laughed out loud. Didn't the pair know they were stopping in one of the most dangerous places in England? Marvelling that two grown men could be so foolish, the thief watched while they tied their horses to a tree. The whole thing was so strange, he didn't leap out and rob them. He wanted to see what they would do.

Before long he had his answer. One of the men took a big black Bible from his saddlebag. Next thing he was speaking in a loud voice to a small crowd. Catchem understood then that the man and his companion were travelling preachers.

More curious than ever, the thief edged closer to hear what the men had to say. They were talking about God's Son, Jesus, he discovered. And soon he was hanging on to their every word. Apparently all through his earthly life this Jesus had gone round forgiving wrongdoers and offering them new life.

'Jesus came into the world to save sinful people – people like you and me,' the preacher explained. 'He can forgive the things we've done wrong. Why not come to him and receive that forgiveness?'

By this time Catchem felt as if the men were speaking directly to him.

'Come to Jesus,' the preacher urged.

So Catchem came – striding out from his hiding-place among the trees.

At first sight of the rough bearded criminal, the crowd

shrank back, their hands tightening nervously around their money bags . . . until they realised they had nothing to fear. Catchem's mask dangled round his neck and his weapon hung loosely at his side. He was kneeling at the roadside, asking for forgiveness.

Once the ex-thief got back on his feet, he didn't waste any time. He went straight back up Hell's Lane to his home in Ettingshall and started spreading the good news.

'Jesus has changed my life and he can change your lives too,' he told all his wicked friends and neighbours.

They laughed to begin with, but that didn't put Catchem off. Some of them got angry, but that didn't put him off either. In the end a few were so impressed with what he said that they became followers of Jesus too.

Years passed and, thanks to the influence of these Christians, the whole village of Ettingshall was transformed. In Hell's Lane a church opened up. Whereas in the past travellers had kept out of the area, it was now safe for them to come and go. And sometimes they would see an upright grey-haired old man standing in Hell's Lane church doorway. 'There's Catchem,' they would say knowingly. 'Before he met Jesus he went around robbing people, but these days he's out to catch 'em for God.'

Teaching point

The effect of spreading God's good news.

Bible reading

Matthew 5:13–16.

Application

After telling the story say that it is a story about change –

about how first one man and then a whole village changed from bad to good. Say that this change came about as a result of people spreading God's good news – first the travelling preachers, then Catchem himself. Finish by reading Matthew 5:13–16 and encouraging the group to spread the good news today.

Songs

Colours of day dawn into the mind (SOFK 14, JP 28)
Come on, let's get up and go (SOFK 16, JP 31)
Go, tell it on the mountain (JP 65)
The fields are white unto harvest time (JP 237)
We've a story to tell to the nations (JP 272)
Hey! Hey! Anybody listening (JP 362)
Let's go and tell our friends that Jesus cares (JP 416)

24. *Happily Ever After*

Hopeful the frog lived in a pond. He had a green speckled body and a loud cheerful croak, and the other pond creatures all looked to him as their leader.

Every morning Hopeful would hop onto a stone at the edge of the water. 'Cheer up! Cheer up!' he would croak loudly. Then he would tell the pond creatures that this might be the day when he changed into a handsome prince. All that was needed was for a beautiful princess to come along and give him a kiss, and immediately his froggy features would disappear, and in their place would come arms and legs and a golden crown. And they would all live happily ever after.

Which was all very well – until, one year, there was a terrible drought. No rain fell for months, and by the end of

June the water level in the pond had dropped so low that its deep places had become shallow and its shallow places had turned into hard, crumbly mud.

'Rain, we need rain,' the pond creatures were moaning. 'If it doesn't rain soon our home will be nothing but a dried-up hole in the ground.'

'Don't worry. I'm a prince in disguise,' Hopeful kept telling them. 'When my beautiful princess comes, we'll all live happily ever after.'

But Hopeful's princess never came. Instead, one evening, as he crouched on his stone, a cat crept out of the bushes. With a rush and a leap it pounced on Hopeful. Next thing the frog found himself pinned to the ground.

'Miaow! I'm going to eat you!' mewed the cat.

'No! No! You can't do that. I'm a prince in disguise,' croaked Hopeful.

'You're a what?'

'A prince in disguise,' the frog repeated. 'Any day now my princess will come. Her kiss will change me into a handsome prince. And we'll all live happily ever after.'

This made the cat laugh in a nasty, superior kind of way.

'My dear frog,' it mewed. 'If you'd spent as much time with humans as I have, you'd know the difference between real life and a fairy tale. Frogs only change into princes in books. Your princess could kiss you until her lips turned green, but you'd be as much of a frog as ever.'

It sniffed Hopeful all over, then mewed on gloomily: 'Real life is no fairy tale. Real life doesn't end with everyone living happily ever after. It ends with ponds drying up and frogs disappearing down cats' throats. You understand?'

Hopeful gulped. He could see that the cat was a great deal bigger than he was, and it had been around a lot longer than he had, and it clearly knew a lot more about life than he did. And if the cat said there wasn't any happily ever after – well, he was in no position to argue. 'Yes,' he gasped.

'I understand. You might as well eat me and get it over with.'

But for some reason the cat seemed to have lost interest. 'I'm sorry. I'm not in the mood to eat you now,' it mewed. 'Talking about life has ruined my appetite.' And it slunk off into the hedge.

Very early next morning, while the rest of the pond creatures were still asleep, Hopeful crawled onto his stone. He hadn't slept a wink all night, and now he looked at the pond and saw, as if for the very first time, how bad things were. With a heavy heart he took it all in – the rock-hard mud, the scorched grass, the wilting pond weeds. 'We can't survive much longer,' he thought to himself. And he knew his fellow creatures would be expecting him to tell them he was a prince in disguise, and they would all live happily ever after. But he couldn't do that any more. Not after talking to the cat.

'Oh, what can I say? What can I say?' he moaned.

And then above his head a soft voice answered, 'I'll tell you what to say, Hopeful.'

It was a cloud.

'Say you were wrong about being a prince in disguise, but you were right about living happily ever after,' the cloud whispered. 'Say that one day the God/Man will return to earth. Say that when he comes there'll be no more cats eating frogs or ponds drying out. Say that everything will be perfect, just the way he meant it to be.'

When Hopeful heard this he blinked back tears.

'Oh I'd love to believe that,' he cried. 'But the cat says. . . .'

'Forget the cat. Cats know something, but not everything,' the cloud laughed. Then its joy spilled over. The first drops fell on Hopeful like a gentle kiss, and then they came faster and harder, pittering, then pattering, then pounding down into the pond.

'Rain! Rain!' cheered the pond creatures.

Full of gratitude, Hopeful looked up.

And there where the cloud had been he saw a rainbow – a glorious rainbow arched across the sky.

Teaching point

The created world – now, and as it will be.

Bible reading

Revelation 21:1–5.

Application

At the end of the story hold up an illustration of a rainbow. Then ask the group if they know how rainbows are made (sunlight reflected by raindrops). Make the point that rainbows are just one of the many beautiful things God created. The trouble is that human sin has resulted in lots of ugly things on earth too (get the group to give illustrations). Some people get sad and discouraged because of these things, but Christians always have a reason for hope. The Bible promises that one day all pain and suffering will end, and creation will be perfect, just the way God meant it to be. Finish by reading Revelation 21:1–5.

Songs

All things bright and beautiful (JP 6)
All around me, Lord, I see Your goodness (JP 7)
For the beauty of the earth (JP 48)
God who made the earth (JP 63)
I have seen the golden sunshine (JP 99)
Morning has broken (JP 166)
Sing we the King who is coming to reign (JP 218)
Who put the colours in the rainbow? (SOFK 191, JP 288)
Can you be sure that the rain will fall? (JP 316)
Don't know much about the ozone layer (JP 328)

JULY

Winners and Losers

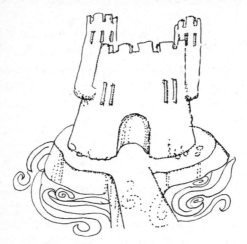

25. Mind Doggs OK

(A true story from the life of George Cadbury)

George Cadbury was a winner – a man who built things to last.

The first thing he built was a sandcastle. He built it one summer afternoon on the beach of the small village of Blackpool. (That's right – 160 years ago Blackpool *was* a small village!) Now, as any holiday-maker will know, you need more than one pair of hands to build a really big sand-castle. So George involved the whole family. His younger brothers and sister hunted the beach for the best building materials – the smoothest stones and the stickiest clay – while he and his two older brothers took charge of the design. All afternoon they worked, fetching and carrying, shaping and piling, until at last their fortress was complete.

The question was: Would it survive the night? Yes! George arrived on the beach next morning to discover that, thanks to their hard work and top quality materials, the Cadbury castle was still standing tall.

The second thing George built was a business. He was twenty-two years old when he and his brother Richard took over the family cocoa factory. At that time it was one of the smallest such businesses in the country, manufacturing a very cheap brand of cocoa – a mixture of cocoa, treacle, flour and potato – and it was losing money.

For three years George and Richard worked and worked. George gave up tea, coffee and the morning paper. He lived on £25 per year, arriving at the factory every morning at 7.00 am and not leaving again until nine o'clock at night. He put every minute of his time, every ounce of his energy, every penny he possessed into looking after his staff and pushing the business forward. But at the end of the third year the business had lost so much money, the brothers were facing ruin.

It was around this time that they decided to stop mixing flour, treacle and potato with their cocoa. From now on, they decided, they would use only the finest ingredients. 'Absolutely pure' would be their motto. The bad news was this meant their cocoa became more expensive. The good news was it tasted great!

And suddenly more people started buying it. Before long the brothers could hardly keep up with the orders, and George found himself running one of the biggest cocoa businesses in the land.

He didn't build a fortune, though. He didn't build a fortune because he used his money to build something else – something which has the same letters as the words Mind Doggs OK. It was a project into which, as usual, he put loads of hard work and top quality ingredients, only this time the ingredients weren't material things like cocoa and sand.

They were spiritual things like pure faith, pure hope and pure love. For George was a follower of Jesus, and his greatest desire was to share his faith and help people have a top quality life.

So, over and over again, George Cadbury proved he knew the secret of building things that would last.

The first thing he built was a sandcastle, and it lasted longer than any other castle on the beach.

The second thing he built was a business – a business which is still going strong to this day.

And, as you know, Mind Doggs OK is an anagram (that's words with the same letters) for the third thing he built. If you haven't worked it out yet, here's another clue: Mind Doggs OK is something a person can build in this life, knowing it will last for ever.

And the answer is: God's kingdom.

Teaching point

The secret of building to last.

Bible reading

Luke 6:47–49.

Telling the story

Before telling the story show the words Mind Doggs OK. Say that you are going to tell a story that will make their meaning clear.

Application

After telling the story remind the group of the three things George Cadbury built and get them to shout out some other things that people can build, e.g. houses, walls, fortunes, friendships. Say that whatever we're building, if we want it to last we'll need to work at it and use good quality materials. Then say that in the Bible Jesus explains the secret of building lives that will last. Read Luke 6:47–49, and ask the group to tell you what the secret is (coming to him, listening to what he has to say and putting his teaching into practice). If we do this we can be sure we are building our lives with top quality materials, and we will live for ever in God's kingdom.

Songs

Don't build your house on the sandy land (SOFK 23, JP 39)
Father hear the prayer we offer (JP 41)
For I'm building a people of power (JP 47)
The wise man built his house upon the rock (JP 252)
The wise may bring their learning (JP 253)
Get up out of bed (JP 343)

26. Watching the Race

Pete and Emma were watching athletics on TV. They liked athletics – especially running.

'There's a holiday Bible club on at the church this afternoon. Are we going?' asked Emma.

'No,' said Pete.

'Why not?' asked Emma.

'Because they'll talk about God. And I'd rather watch telly. I want to see who wins this race,' replied Pete.

'That reminds me of a story,' a voice spoke up from behind a newspaper. The voice belonged to their grandad.

'Not now, Grandad,' muttered Pete. But Grandad had already tossed his paper aside. Once he'd been reminded of a story there was no stopping him.

146

'As far as I know it's a true story,' he began. 'I heard it from a friend down at the lunch club. It was about this lad called Jimmy who was a very strong runner. And he was in a big stadium taking part in a very important race.'

'Like the one we're trying to watch,' said Pete pointedly, his eyes glued to the TV.

'Right. And the race he was taking part in was another one where the competitors keep going round and round the track.'

'The 10,000 metres,' said Pete.

'Most likely. Anyway, the starting pistol fired, and away Jimmy went. And of course there were other runners all around him . . . quite a few of them ahead . . . some behind. And the sports stadium was full of spectators, chatting and fanning themselves with their programmes. It was just the beginning of a very long race, you see, so they weren't getting too worked up. And then, suddenly, this voice rings out: "Come on! Go for it, Jimmy!" And the crowd look round to see who's doing all the shouting, and it turns out to be this little red-faced man with a beard, hopping up and down in his seat as if he has ants in his pants. . . .'

'Jimmy's grandad!' winked Emma.

'No,' said Grandad. 'Jimmy's coach. "Come on, Jimmy! Go for it, Jimmy!" He just keeps right on yelling encouragement . . . lap after lap after lap. And sure enough, as the race goes on Jimmy begins to gain ground. And the coach is getting more and more excited. "Yes! That's my boy! You can do it!" A few more laps and there's just Jimmy and one other lad leading the field. Neck and neck, they are. Everyone can see that one of the two is going to win that race.'

'And if Jimmy's coach has anything to do with it, it's going to be Jimmy. Right?' Pete was interested now.

'Right. "Come on, Jimmy! You can do it, Jimmy. . . ." The coach is still cheering his head off. And Jimmy pulls out ahead of his rival. The coach's enthusiasm infects the whole crowd, and they all get behind Jimmy. "Jim–my, Jim–my, Jim–my," they're chanting. Well, the two lads come into the final lap and Jimmy has a commanding lead. He's way out in front, charging along, with a whole stadium full of supporters all encouraging him at the top of their voices. And then, ten strides away from the finishing line, he stops.'

'He *what*?' cried Pete and Emma.

'He stops,' said Grandad. 'The crowd can hardly believe it. The cheering dies away, and there's this eerie silence . . . only broken by the sound of a little red-faced man with a beard having a nervous breakdown in the grandstand: "No, Jimmy!" he groans. "You've got to finish the race! Don't stop now! Keep going!"'

'But Jimmy doesn't keep going. He just smiles up at his coach, and then he waves at the crowd. Then he turns round. And there's the other guy, stumbling up behind him. And Jimmy simply holds out his hand.'

There was a moment of silence. Then Grandad went on quietly. 'He knew what he was doing. He hadn't lost sight of the finishing line or misunderstood the rules. He'd stopped on purpose – and he stood there waiting, with his arm outstretched, until the other lad drew alongside him and took his hand. And then, hand in hand, the pair of them crossed the finishing line together.'

'Wow! Magic!' Pete nodded approvingly.

'The crowd certainly thought so. They raised the roof with their cheers. And Jimmy's coach came down from the grandstand. He went over to the finishing line and clapped Jimmy on the shoulder. "Jimmy, you're a *real* winner," he said.'

'Good old Jimmy!' Emma was as impressed as her brother.

'Good old Jimmy!' Grandad agreed. 'But you know, when I heard that story, I couldn't help thinking about the other lad. And I thought how different the ending would have been if Jimmy had held out his hand and the other guy had refused to take it.'

'He'd have been mad!' exclaimed Pete.

His grandfather smiled. 'And then I thought: there's someone waiting for us with an outstretched hand – waiting to share his victory; a victory over sin, a victory over death. . . .'

There was another silence.

Emma glanced at Pete, who got up and set the video.

'Cheers, Grandad,' the boy grinned. 'We're off out to the holiday Bible club. We'll watch the end of the race later.'

Teaching point

In the race of life, Jesus wants us to share his victory.

Bible readings

Hebrews 12:1–2; 1 Corinthians 15:55–56.

Application

Before telling the story read Hebrews 12:1–2 and ask the group which race is being pictured here (the race of life).

After telling the story read 1 Corinthians 15:55–56 (verses in which the apostle Paul thanks God for the victory which is ours in Christ). Finish with a prayer thanking Jesus for all he has done and for the victory he wants to share with us.

Songs

Be bold, be strong, for the Lord your God is with you
    (SOFK 6, JP 14)
God sent His Son, they call Him Jesus (JP 58)
I am trusting You, Lord Jesus (JP 86)
I can run through a troop (JP 90)

In the name of Jesus (JP 111)
I want to walk with Jesus Christ (SOFK 100, JP 124)
May the mind of Christ my Saviour (JP 165)
Now be strong and very courageous (JP 172)
Turn your eyes upon Jesus (JP 260)

27. In Training

(A story from the life of Eric Liddell)

Just before the 1924 Olympics a young Christian athlete made a difficult decision. Eric Liddell knew he had a good chance of winning a gold medal in the 100-metre sprint. But as soon as he heard that the heats were being held on a Sunday, he pulled out of the race. He decided that it would be wrong to run on the Lord's Day – so he didn't. But that wasn't the end of the story. Not running in the 100-metre sprint (the race which he *thought* he ran best) meant Eric entered for a race he would never have dreamed of trying otherwise: the 400 metres. And to everyone's delight and amazement, he won!

Twenty years later Eric Liddell was a prisoner. He had spent the years since winning his Olympic Gold working as a missionary in China. Then, during the Second World War, he was sent, along with hundreds of other Westerners, to Weihsien prison camp – a horrible place where no one had enough food or space, and mosquitoes and flies were everywhere.

People found it hard to get on with each other in such miserable conditions. Quarrels and arguments were always breaking out. But everyone could see that Eric was different. He did all he could to make life better for others. He chopped wood for the old people, he visited the sick, and he took a special interest in the children and teenagers. Every day, except Sunday, he would organise sports and activities for them – chess, draughts, rounders, softball. Nothing was too much trouble. Every day, except Sunday, he could be found in the games room, helping them build a model or set up some sort of competition.

Then one Sunday a group of bored teenagers decided to organise a hockey match. They fetched the battered hockey sticks from the games room, and divided themselves into two teams – boys against girls.

The match began. But soon there was an argument, and without a referee to settle it, the game turned ugly. The teenagers attacked each other with their sticks.

'Toads!' the girls shouted.

'Birdbrains!' the boys yelled back.

The result? Well, there certainly weren't any winners. Just bruised shins, damaged equipment and a lot of bad feeling.

During the week that followed, Eric did his best to calm things down. He tore up one of his few remaining sheets to fix the damaged hockey sticks, winding the linen strips around the cracked blades. But he couldn't mend the divisions between the teenagers. The bruises and cracks in good relationships were still plain to see.

'We'll get our own back,' the girls were vowing.

'No you won't – *birdbrains*!'

'Yes we will – *toads*!'

At 6.00 am the following Sunday Eric got up to read his Bible and pray. He did this every morning, keeping a notebook on the table beside him in which he would jot down anything he felt God was telling him to do. There was one problem which was very much on his mind that morning: the hockey match. 'Lord, don't let it be the same as last week,' he prayed as the sun rose and his dormitory mates slept on.

A few hours later the match began. Boys and girls, armed with their newly mended hockey sticks, faced each other on the makeshift hockey pitch – just as they had done seven days before. But this week things were different. The game went smoothly. There was no arguing. No cheating. The two teams stayed friends.

A real answer to prayer, you may be thinking! And indeed it was. But there's a little bit more to the story. As Eric had prayed and thought the matter over, he'd come to a decision. It would be wrong to leave the young people to fight and argue, he'd decided. So that week he'd been on the hockey pitch with them – keeping Sunday special by refereeing the match.

Teaching point

Spiritual discipline.

Bible reading

1 Corinthians 9:24–27.

Application

After telling the story, show the group a medal or cup (ideally something you have won yourself). Then ask them: What was the top award that Eric Liddell won? Agree that his Olympic gold medal was a very high award, but it wasn't his top award. Introduce the Bible passage as a reading which tells us what it was, i.e. a crown that will last for ever. Point out that just as athletes must train hard to win, so Eric saw his need for spiritual training, which included Bible reading and prayer. How much spiritual training do we do?

Songs

In our work and in our play (JP 108)
I want to walk with Jesus Christ (SOFK 100, JP 124)
May the mind of Christ my Saviour (JP 165)
Now be strong and very courageous (JP 172)
This little light of mine, I'm gonna let it shine (JP 258)
Everywhere He walks with me (JP 334)
Have you got an appetite? (SOFK 52, JP 357)
I'm going to hide God's word inside my heart (JP 378)
I'm going to say my prayers (SOFK 89, JP 379)
I'm going to set my heart (JP 382)

28. A Tale of Two Kings

One day King Ahab of Israel and King Jehoshaphat of Judah met up in Samaria. For many years their kingdoms had been at war, but now they'd decided to live in peace for a change. The whole idea of the meeting was for them to make plans for the future, and King Ahab knew exactly what he wanted. . . .

'Now that we are no longer enemies, I suppose you could say we are friends,' he began, as they settled themselves comfortably in their thrones.

'You could indeed,' King Jehoshaphat agreed.

'Which means that your hopes have become my hopes and my hopes have become your hopes,' King Ahab went on.

'That's right,' King Jehoshaphat nodded.

King Ahab took a deep breath, leaned over and came straight to the point: 'Well, my hope is to win back the city of Ramoth Gilead from those nasty Syrians. So how about us launching a joint attack?'

King Jehoshaphat tugged at his beard. Of course he knew that joint attacks were the sort of thing friends did together. 'Your hopes are my hopes, my people are your people and my horses are your horses,' he said slowly.

'That's settled then,' cheered Ahab. 'We'll go into battle tomorrow.'

'Er . . . not so fast,' Jehoshaphat said. He was a godly man and didn't believe in rushing into things. 'Before I go into battle, I always check it out with God.'

'Oh me too,' King Ahab said, trying his best to look enthusiastic. In fact he was not at all godly, but checking things out with God wasn't a problem – not when his checker-outers were a band of prophets who could be relied on to say exactly what he wanted to hear.

So he sent for them.

'King Jehoshaphat and I have just dreamed up a real winner of a plan to recapture Ramoth Gilead from the Syrians,' he announced. 'We've brought you here to answer a question. Should we go to war or not?'

Well, it was a bit like putting coins into a hot drinks machine. The band of prophets whirled around, gurgling noisily, then swooshed out their answer.

'Go to war!' they shouted. 'God will give you victory!'

'Excellent! God is definitely with us on this!' said Ahab. He turned to his ally with a grin.

But King Jehoshaphat was still tugging his beard. 'Back home in Judah, I do things differently,' he murmured. 'I send for a true prophet of the Lord – someone with real spiritual power. Aren't there any prophets like that in Samaria?'

'Well . . . there's Micaiah, the son of Imlah,' Ahab sighed. He knew from experience that Micaiah had the awkward habit of actually listening to God. 'But to be honest, I can't stand the fellow. He never prophesies anything good about me.'

'You shouldn't say that,' Jehoshaphat said, looking shocked.

'Send for Micaiah, the son of Imlah,' Ahab told a messenger quickly.

A short time later Micaiah arrived, having been well-warned by the messenger to mind his manners and agree with everything the other prophets had said.

Ahab gave him a meaningful look. 'Micaiah,' he asked smoothly, 'should we attack Ramoth Gilead?'

For a moment the man of God was silent.

'Att-*ack* Ra-moth Gil-e-ad, and be vic-*tor*-ious,' the prophetic band were chanting in the background.

'Att-*ack* Ra-moth Gil-e-ad, and be vic-*tor*- ious,' parroted Micaiah.

King Ahab scowled. 'Come on, Micaiah. Make it more convincing.'

'Oh, all right then.' Micaiah took a deep breath and spoke out in ringing tones: 'I see Israelite soldiers wandering hopelessly about in the hills and I hear a voice saying: "These men have lost their leader. Let them go home in peace."'

Jehoshaphat gulped and nudged Ahab, saying, 'That sounds as if your life is in danger.'

'What did I tell you!' Ahab stamped his foot. 'The fellow *never* prophesies anything good about me.'

But there was more. Micaiah turned round and pointed to the court prophets. 'What these men are saying is false,' he proclaimed. 'A lying spirit is speaking through them.'

Needless to say this infuriated King Ahab. 'Take Micaiah off to jail and give him nothing to eat but bread and water until I get back from the battlefield,' he yelled.

'You mean we're still going to war?' gulped King Jehoshaphat.

King Ahab nodded. 'Look, let's be sensible about it. We've heard hundreds of prophets predicting victory and only one predicting defeat. So clearly our attack on Ramoth Gilead should go ahead.'

Accordingly, a few days later, the two kings went into battle. You can probably guess what happened.

Just as Micaiah had said, King Ahab was fatally wounded in the fight. He lived long enough to see his army defeated, and then he died.

As for King Jehoshaphat, well, there's an interesting extra bit to his story. On his way home to Jerusalem, he was met by one of his own prophets. 'God is angry with you,' the prophet said bluntly. 'You shouldn't have got involved with that evil king.'

And the interesting thing is how Jehoshaphat reacted. Unlike Ahab he didn't turn round and have the prophet flung into jail. Instead he took his words to heart and made up his mind to be more careful in future. And the Bible tells us that he rode back to his palace and reigned peacefully over Judah for the rest of his days.

Teaching point

The importance of listening to God.

Bible readings

This story is based on 1 Kings 22:1–40 and 2 Chronicles 18 and 19:1–3.

Telling the story

Use illustrations of the two kings while telling the story. Alternatively, arrange for helpers to dress up as the two kings and mime the parts.

Application

After telling the story hold up the illustration of King Ahab (or bring forward the character). Get the group to cheer if they think Ahab was a winner and hiss if he was a loser. Ask someone who hissed to say what Ahab lost and why he lost it (his life, because he refused to listen to God). What about King Jehoshaphat? Was he a winner or a loser? Aim to bring out the fact that the Bible paints Jehoshaphat as a winner because, although he made mistakes, he really wanted to obey God. Finish by discussing briefly how God speaks to us today (through the Bible, through conscience, through other Christians). The question is: Do we really want to hear and obey him?

Songs

Isaiah heard the voice of the Lord (JP 114)
Make the book live to me, O Lord (JP 163)
Seek ye first (SOFK 154, JP 215)
The best book to read is the Bible (JP 234)
We have heard a joyful sound (JP 266)
Father, Your Word is like a light in the darkness (JP 338)
Hey! Hey! Anybody listening? (JP 362)
I'm going to hide God's Word inside my heart (JP 378)

AUGUST

The Great Escape

(A Five-Part Serial)

29. Part One: Slave Labour

This is a story about four children: Benji, Deborah, Miriam and Jake. Like any group of children they had different looks and personalities. Ten-year-old Benji was tall for his age and easy-going, while his nine-year-old sister Deborah was small, with a hot temper. Quiet, pretty Miriam had a stubborn streak, and Jake, her eleven-year-old brother, was a born schemer, always wheeling and dealing. The main thing the four had in common was that they were all slaves – Israelite slaves living in Egypt 3,000 years ago.

As far as the children were concerned being slaves meant lots of hard work. It meant the boys being forced to spend their time making bricks (a dusty, back-breaking job). It meant the girls doing everything that needed to be done at home – the cooking, the cleaning, the washing – while their mothers were at the beck and call of Egyptian mistresses.

Still, despite their slavery, they had their hopes and dreams. Deborah dreamed of adventure and having lots of jewellery (like the Egyptian princess her mother served). Miriam dreamed of getting married. Jake dreamed of making money. And Benji dreamed of winning a bronze star in the brickfields. (Bronze stars were awarded every month by the foremen in the brickfields to the Israelite slave in each group who'd made the most bricks.)

And one day it seemed as if Benji's dream was about to come true.

'The stars are being handed out tomorrow,' the boy told his sister after work. 'And guess what! I haven't exactly counted, but my pile of bricks seems bigger than anyone else's.'

Deborah's heart leapt. She was almost as keen for Benji to win a star as Benji was. 'So you think your pile is bigger than Jake's this month?' she beamed. (Jake was an expert brick-maker, and Miriam was always boasting about the three bronze stars he had won.)

Benji nodded. 'Unless he's got some extra bricks hidden away somewhere. He's so sneaky, I wouldn't put it past him.'

'You don't really think that!' said Deborah. She could tell from the way Benji spoke that he was sure of success.

She got up next morning full of excitement. For once she had something to look forward to. She hummed as she packed up a hunk of bread for her brother's lunch. 'Good luck!' she said, her eyes sparkling as she handed it to him.

'Thanks,' Benji nodded.

'You're going to win. I just know it,' Deborah told him.

She spent the rest of the day dreaming about the bronze star, hoping it would be a nice shiny one. It would be like having her first piece of real jewellery. She planned to tie it onto a leather thong and wear it round her neck – the way

Miriam did. Except, of course, Miriam had three stars on her thong, and the sound of them clinking together made Deborah green with envy. But at least this month's star would be hers.

As usual, just before sunset when her mother came home, Deborah put on her cloak and skipped next door to collect Miriam. The two girls always went together to meet their brothers coming back from work. 'Ready?' she called brightly.

'Of course,' Miriam said, stepping out to join her friend. Clink . . . clink . . . clink went the bronze pieces round her neck, but Deborah didn't care.

'Benji's won the star this month,' she smiled.

'How do you know that?' Miriam looked mildly surprised. 'Did he send you a message?'

'No. I just know something wonderful has happened,' Deborah beamed. 'I feel it in my bones.'

'Your bones must be different from mine,' Miriam shrugged. 'I don't get those kinds of feelings.'

There was no time for further discussion, because at that moment their brothers came into view. Hurrah! Deborah rushed up the street to greet Benji.

'Well?' she smiled up expectantly.

'I'm sorry, Deb,' Benji said sheepishly. 'Half of my bricks fell apart. I didn't mix enough straw with the mud.'

Jake, meanwhile, had taken his bundle from his shoulders. He was opening it up and handing something to Miriam. 'Another star to add to your collection,' he said proudly.

What?! Deborah's lower lip started to tremble. She couldn't help it. Next thing she knew she had burst into floods of tears. But she wasn't just crying about lumps of polished metal. She was crying because she'd been so sure something wonderful was about to happen, and it hadn't. Nothing had changed. Things were exactly the same today as they had been yesterday. The same as they would be tomorrow and the next day and the next. . . .

'I hate us being slaves here in Egypt,' she sobbed. 'I hate you having to make bricks all day. I hate living with people who laugh at our religion and have no time for our God.'

'Shhh, Deb! Someone's coming. Keep your voice down!' Benji hissed.

But it was too late. The tall stranger coming towards them down the street had clearly overheard every word.

'So, child, you hate being a slave in Egypt, do you?' a voice rang out.

Deborah looked up through her tears and saw an elderly man of noble bearing. For a horrible moment she thought he was one of Pharaoh's court officials. And then she saw that he was a fellow Israelite, and that his eyes were kind.

'Yes,' she muttered.

'So what would you say if I told you that God – the God of our ancestors Abraham, Isaac and Jacob – has seen how cruelly we are being treated here, and that he has sent me here to tell you he is about to bring us out into a rich, fertile land of our own?'

The moment Deborah heard those words, her tears dried up. 'I'd say it was the best news I'd ever heard!' she gasped.

'God bless you, child,' the stranger smiled and moved off.

'Please, wait! We don't even know your name,' yelled Benji, full of curiosity, bounding after him.

'It's Moses,' the stranger called over his shoulder without stopping.

'His name is Moses,' Benji announced as he rejoined his friends.

'Moses!' Deborah gave a little hop of excitement. 'Imagine! We've just bumped into the man God's sent to rescue us. I *knew* something wonderful would happen today.'

Teaching point

God wants to set us free.

Bible reading

John 8:34–36. The background to this story is found in
Exodus 1:8–22 and Exodus 3:4–9.

Application

After telling the fictional story, show picture illustrations of
some things people long for today. Ask the group for further
suggestions of things their own age group want, e.g. a particular make of trainers, the latest computer game. Remind
them how, in the story, Deborah really wanted some jewellery. Wanting things is part of human nature. We have to
be careful though, because we can easily become slaves to
our wants and desires – that is, they order us around! What's
more, the Bible says that everyone who sins is a sort of slave,
being bossed around by their human nature. Introduce the
work and person of Jesus by saying that just as God sent
Moses to free his people from slavery in Egypt, so he has sent
someone who can free us from that sort of slavery today.
Read John 8:34–36 and encourage the group to say who that
person is.

Songs

Brothers and sisters (JP 21)
Come on, let's get up and go (SOFK 16, JP 31)
Hark the glad sound! The Saviour comes (JP 68)
I will sing, I will sing a song unto the Lord (SOFK 104,
    JP 126)
Thank You, for ev'ry new good morning (JP 230)
Thank You, Lord, for this fine day (SOFK 160, JP 232)
When Israel was in Egypt's land (JP 276)
Everywhere He walks with me (JP 334)

30. Part Two: Courtyard Quarrel

A few days later Moses called all the Israelite leaders to a meeting. Deborah and Benji's dad, Simeon, went along, and came home bursting with news.

'Praise God!' he said. 'Praise God! He has seen how cruelly we are being treated here in Egypt and has sent someone to lead us to freedom.'

He went on to tell the children all about Moses – who he was and what he'd said. 'Gosh! Really?' Deborah and Benji stood there doing their best to look as if he wasn't telling them about someone they'd already met.

'It was his brother Aaron who did the talking,' Simeon explained. 'People didn't know what to think at first. I mean, it just seemed too good to be true. So Moses gave us signs to prove he really *had* been sent by God. He threw his staff onto the ground and it changed into a snake. Then he picked the snake up by the tail and it changed back into a staff again.'

'Wow!' the children gasped, eyes widening with amazement.

'Tomorrow he's going to get Pharaoh's permission for us to go and worship God in the desert,' Simeon finished. 'It's the first step to freedom.'

Next morning everyone was far too excited to work. Not a single Israelite slave headed off for the brickfields.

'We're leaving. God has said so. We're leaving. God has said so,' Deborah chanted as she brushed round the small courtyard outside her home. A moment later Miriam came out, and the two friends started their favourite game of hopscotch. Before long Benji was outside too, with baby Nathan in his arms.

The fact that he'd actually brought the baby outdoors showed just how confident everyone was feeling. Normally baby boys were kept well hidden. Pharaoh, the King of Egypt, was trying to cut down the number of Israelites living in the land, and his latest scheme for doing this had been to order his people to snatch Israelite babies and throw them into the River Nile. Of course many Egyptians ignored the command, but Deborah's family still feared for Nathan's life.

Today though that dark cloud had lifted and the baby was outside with Benji, enjoying the sun.

'Am I glad the desert isn't paved,' the boy teased. 'I won't have to watch you two playing that stupid game.'

'Hey! It takes real skill to get the stones onto the right square,' cried Deborah. 'I bet you couldn't do it.'

'I could too.' Benji took up the challenge. Next thing he had left the baby lying on his tummy on a mat, and was trying to beat the girls.

Suddenly a smug voice interrupted their fun. 'Look what I've got!'

Benji spun round and there was Jake, strolling across the courtyard with a bowl. With a swagger, he set it down on the square Benji had been targeting with his stone.

'What is it?' asked Deborah.

'Honey,' said Jake. 'Help yourselves. I'm full.'

Immediately it was all fingers to the bowl as Benji, Deborah and Miriam scooped up the golden syrup.

'So where did it come from?' Deborah enquired stickily.

Jake looked mysterious. 'That's for me to know and you to find out,' he said. 'I'll tell you one thing though. There will be no more sitting round honey-pots if your friend Moses has his way and drags us all off into the desert.'

Deborah spluttered. 'Moses *isn't* dragging us off into the desert. He's leading us into a land of our own – a land *flowing* with milk and honey.'

'Sure . . . sure. That's what he *says*,' shrugged Jake. 'But the fact is, if you walk out of Egypt tomorrow, you'll be exchanging shady courtyards and pools and the vineyards for the burning heat of a desert full of snakes and scorpions, with no water and only as much food as you can carry.'

Deborah hesitated. If there was one thing she hated, it was snakes.

'Don't forget God will be with us,' Benji broke in. 'And I reckon freedom in the desert is a hundred times better than honey as a slave. And here's another thing,' he warmed to the theme. 'We don't spend our days sitting in shady courtyards gorging ourselves on honey. Most of the time we're sweating away in the brickfields. And we're always worrying about an Egyptian official snatching Nathan and throwing him into the. . . .'

'Hey, wait a minute! Where *is* Nathan?' Deborah interrupted.

'Lying on the mat,' said Benji.

'No! Look! He's gone!' Deborah's face went white. 'Someone must have taken him. He can't crawl yet. This is all your fault, Jake.' She turned on the older boy. 'You were given the honey by some of your fine Egyptian friends, weren't you? And now they've sneaked up behind our backs and snatched my baby brother. I wouldn't be surprised if you'd even arranged it with them. Have they paid you, Jake? We know how keen you are on making money.'

Even as she spoke, a baby started to wail.

Benji was first inside the house. 'It's all right. He's in here playing with Mum's cooking pots,' he called. Next thing he was back in the courtyard clutching Nathan. 'Who said the little rascal couldn't crawl?'

'Who said my brother was a traitor?' said Miriam coldly.

Deborah felt ashamed. 'Sorry,' she muttered.

But Jake and Miriam were in no mood to accept her apology. 'That's just you and your brother all over. Shout first, think later,' Jake sneered. 'Maybe now you'll think about what I said before you rush off after Moses. Come along, Miriam.' And the pair stalked off.

'Ooops!' Benji pulled a funny face. 'Looks like you've just lost a friend. When will you learn to control that temper of yours?'

The quarrel cast a shadow over the rest of the day.

And there was more bad news when their father came home for supper.

'Moses and Aaron went in to see Pharaoh, but he refused to let us go,' he told them soberly. 'He's ordered everyone back to work tomorrow.'

The children exchanged looks of dismay.

'Mind you,' Simeon added. 'Moses isn't taking "no" for an answer.'

After supper that evening Benji and Deborah had a quick chat before bed. Benji had noticed that his sister was unusually quiet.

'You're thinking about what Jake said, aren't you?'

Deborah nodded.

'So if Moses *does* manage to get Pharaoh's permission, will you still want to leave Egypt?'

'Of course I will,' Deborah declared. 'I mean, if we stay here we'll be slaves for the rest of our lives.' She paused, before adding softly, 'I just hope Miriam and Jake will come too.'

Teaching point

We shouldn't let anything hold us back on the road to freedom.

Bible reading

Luke 18:18–30. The background to this story is found in Exodus 4:29–31 and Exodus 5:1–5.

Application

After telling the fictional story, show the group a hair band, a plug and a piece of barbed wire, and ask what they have in common (they're all designed to hold things back). Then say that in the story two things were holding Jake back from leaving Egypt. One was Pharaoh. What was the other? (Things he didn't want to give up.) Introduce the New Testament reading (the story of the rich young ruler) as a story of a young man with the same problem. The disciples, on the other hand, didn't allow anything to hold them back from following Jesus. Encourage the group to think of the sorts of things that can hold people back from following Jesus today (afraid of being laughed at, of losing friends, of Jesus asking them to give up some things they enjoy, etc.). At the end of today's fiction story, Deborah hoped to persuade her friends that they didn't want to be slaves for the rest of their lives. What might we say to persuade someone to follow Jesus?

Songs

Be bold, be strong, for the Lord your God is with you
  (SOFK 6, JP 14)
Come on, let's get up and go (SOFK 16, JP 31)
Happiness is to know the Saviour (JP 70)
I do not know what lies ahead (JP 92)
If you want joy, real joy, wonderful joy (JP 96)
I have decided to follow Jesus (JP 98)
I met Jesus at the crossroads (JP 102)
I want to live for Jesus ev'ry day (ev'ry day) (JP 122)
I want to walk with Jesus Christ (SOFK 100, JP 124)
I've come to a time when I must change (JP 383)

31. Part Three: Nothing But Trouble

Next morning, on her way to fetch water, Deborah planned how she would make things up with Miriam. 'Me and my big mouth!' she was going to say. 'I should have known Jake would never side with the Egyptians. I'm *really* sorry.'

She hoped that would be enough to put things right between them, but on reaching the spring, there was no sign of her friend.

'Never mind,' thought Deborah. 'I'll see her at the market.'

She saw Miriam at the market all right – bent over a pile of melons on the other side of the square. 'Yoohoo! Miriam!' she called, jumping up and down, waving and trying to attract her friend's attention. But Miriam didn't

173

look round and by the time Deborah reached the melon stall, she had gone.

'Never mind,' Deborah shrugged. 'I'll say sorry this evening when we go to meet Benji and Jake.'

Towards sunset Deborah called next door as usual. 'You're too late,' a neighbour shouted across the street. 'Miriam left early today.'

Oh dear! Deborah had to face the fact that Miriam was avoiding her.

Worse was to come. The Benji she met a few minutes later was a very different lad from the cheery joker who'd left the house that morning. His head was down, his expression was grim, and he was dragging his feet as if he'd lost all his energy.

'What's the matter? You look wrecked,' said Deborah.

'It's the slave-drivers!' the boy muttered. 'Instead of giving us the straw for our bricks as usual, they told us to go and gather it up for ourselves. Then at the end of the day they started yelling because we hadn't made enough bricks.'

'But you can't make the same number of bricks with no straw!' cried Deborah.

'Try telling them that.'

Deborah sighed and Benji stamped hard on an over-ripe fig, pretending it was a slave-driver. Really, what with problems at home and problems at work, it had been a rotten day all round.

And the next day was a complete nightmare.

'We worked non-stop with no breaks – not even a few minutes for lunch,' groaned Benji. 'We gathered straw all morning, then rushed back to the brickfields and made as many bricks as we could. But it was nowhere near the usual number, so the slave-drivers turned round and punished our foremen. . . .'

'They *what*?!'

'They beat the foremen,' Benji repeated flatly. 'Joash,

Jethro and Micah got ten lashes each. I hate to think what will happen tomorrow.'

Tomorrow was washing day – the day when the women took their laundry down to the River Nile. Usually Deborah worked alongside Miriam, but since she still hadn't managed to get their friendship back on track, she found herself scrubbing and rinsing alone. It made her feel awful, especially when Miriam walked straight past her with two other girls and sat down between them on the bank.

Everyone was up in arms about what had been happening in the brickfields.

'It's so cruel and unfair!' one of Miriam's new friends moaned.

'Pharaoh is making our lives more of a misery than ever!' sighed the other.

'And you know whose fault *that* is,' Miriam said quietly but forcefully. 'My brother says that man Moses is to blame. He says Pharaoh is making life so difficult for us because Moses keeps pestering him to let us go and worship God in the desert. He says that since Moses arrived, we've had nothing but trouble. . . .'

Nothing but trouble. The words seemed to echo on in Deborah's mind after the chattering group had wrung out their washing and left. Sadly and thoughtfully the girl gathered up her basket of wet clothes. She had to admit it *did* seem as if God's plan had gone wrong.

'I'm so confused,' she told Benji that night. 'Two days ago I believed God had heard our prayers and sent Moses to rescue us. But now I don't know what's going on.'

'Me neither,' Benji shrugged.

For a moment the brother and sister looked at each other hopelessly, until Deborah gave a slight toss of her head. 'I've just had an idea!' she exclaimed. 'Why don't we go and talk to him!'

Benji frowned. 'Talk to whom?'

'To Moses, of course. He's only staying a few streets away. We could go round really early in the morning. Before anyone else is awake. . . .'

'Sure, and after we've talked to Moses, we could have a little heart-to-heart with Pharaoh. . . .'

'Benji, I mean it.'

'Oh, all right then.'

Suddenly talking to Moses seemed like a good idea to Benji too.

So very early next morning, while the stars were still glittering diamonds in a black velvet sky, the children slipped out of the house and made their way along the narrow city streets. Within a few minutes they were tapping on the door of a mud-brick building.

Moses himself answered their knock. 'We meet again, my young friends,' he smiled, clearly not in the least put out to find two children on his doorstep. 'What can I do for you?'

'We've come because we're confused,' said Deborah. 'You told us God had sent you to lead us to freedom, but now everything's gone wrong. Pharaoh won't let us go and he's treating us worse than ever. . . .'

'So you're wondering if I've made a big mistake. Is that it?' Moses finished.

'Well, yes . . . actually.'

The old man nodded. 'I've been wondering the same myself.'

'Really?!'

'Yesterday I felt just like you do now. I mean, I knew what Pharaoh had been up to, and how the Israelite elders were wishing I'd never gone anywhere near him. So I spent last night talking to God. . . .' He paused, and the children saw his face light up with the memory.

'What happened? What did God say?' they prompted.

'He said that he had everything under control and that he was about to show his power to the Egyptians.'

'He said that?'

Moses nodded, and looking at his face the children had no doubt that what he had told them was true. 'Wow!'

Outside a cock crowed. It was time to go. But that one brief conversation had certainly been worth losing sleep for. Deborah felt as if a heavy weight had rolled off her shoulders. 'Talking to you has made such a difference,' she told Moses as they stepped back into the street.

'Yeah,' agreed Benji. 'It's brilliant knowing God's in control.'

'You can say that again,' said Moses, giving him a meaningful wink. 'So this evening, on your way home from work, go and look at the river.'

Teaching point

When things go wrong, prayer (i.e. talking and listening to God) can make a real difference.

Bible reading

Mark 1:35–37. The background to this story is found in Exodus 5, Exodus 6:1–12 and Exodus 7:1–5.

Application

Focus on times when life is tough – times when we feel like running away. (You could lead into this with a question/joke: Why did Cinderella lose the football match? Answer: Because her coach was a pumpkin and she ran away from the ball!) Remind the group that when life got really tough for Deborah and for Moses, they made a wise decision. What did they do? (They talked to someone who could help.) Encourage the children to identify people with whom they can talk over problems. Point out that while human beings may be able to help in some situations but not in others, God is *always* able to help. Read the New Testament passage, which speaks of Jesus praying all night to God. As we journey with him on the road to freedom, we too will discover the power of prayer.

Songs

Ask! Ask! Ask! (JP 11)
Daniel was a man of prayer (JP 36)
Father I place into Your hands (SOFK 28, JP 42)
Our Father who is in heaven (JP 192)
What a friend we have in Jesus (JP 273)
I'm going to say my prayers (JP 379)
Did you ever talk to God above (JP 329)
God has made me, and He knows me (JP 346)
His ways are not our ways (JP 364)
I cast all my cares upon You (JP 369)
Prayer is like a telephone (SOFK 148, JP 448)
When I'm feeling lonely, when I'm feeling blue (JP 493)
When the dark clouds are above you (JP 494)

32. Part Four: Ten Plagues and a Plot

'Go and look at the river,' Moses had said.

Deborah and Benji didn't know what to expect, but even before they reached the Nile that evening, it was clear that something was going on. A large crowd of people had gathered along the river bank and were talking excitedly in small groups.

As the children approached, they bumped into one of their cousins. 'What's happened? Why is everyone down here?' Benji asked.

'They've come to look at the water. Moses has turned it into blood.'

'Blood!' gasped Deborah.

'That's right. He did it this morning. He went to see

179

Pharaoh at his favourite river bathing spot and told him that God really means business. Then he raised his staff and . . . well . . . go and see for yourselves.'

The children pushed on through the crowd to the water's edge.

Sure enough, the normally blue river was now a murky brownish red.

'Pooh!' Deborah held her nose. 'It smells horrible!'

'One thing's certain. No one will be drinking that,' agreed Benji. 'And I wouldn't give much for the fishes' chances of survival.'

The children looked at each other in delight. 'Well, this just *proves* God really is speaking through Moses,' crowed Deborah. 'Pharaoh will have to let us go now.'

'I wouldn't count on it,' said a voice.

It was Jake. Deborah and Benji had been so taken up with the colour and smell of the water, they hadn't noticed him.

'You haven't heard the end of the story,' Jake continued in his usual know-it-all tone. 'Pharaoh didn't pay Moses any more attention after this bit of hocus-pocus than he did before. He just turned on his heel and marched back into the palace. In other words, he doesn't think this river stunt proves that God is speaking to him. He just thinks it proves your Moses is a talented magician.'

'But . . . but . . . that's *crazy*!' Deborah spluttered.

Jake shrugged. 'Well it makes sense to me. Business as usual – that's my motto. I plan to make the most of this water shortage.'

'What do you mean?' said Benji sharply.

'That's for me to know and you to find out,' replied Jake, turning on his heel and leaving Deborah and Benji to consider the stinking red river.

'You'd think anyone would realise this wasn't some sort of magic trick,' Deborah fumed. 'It makes me wonder if

Pharaoh has a problem with his ears, the way he refuses to listen to God.'

But the problem wasn't with Pharaoh's ears. It was with his heart.

Nine times over the next few months Moses went to the Egyptian ruler. And nine times Pharaoh hardened his heart and refused to let the Israelites go. And every time he hardened his heart, something very unpleasant happened. The plague of blood was followed by a plague of frogs. The frogs were followed by gnats. And the gnats were followed by flies. When the flies were swarming all over the palace, Pharaoh did agree that the Israelites could leave, but the moment the flies buzzed off, he hardened his heart again. So the plagues continued. Thousands of the Egyptians' horses, camels, donkeys, cattle, sheep and goats took sick and died. Next the people and their animals came out in horrible boils. Then all their flax and barley was destroyed in the worst ever hailstorm and any remaining grass in their fields or fruit on their trees was gobbled up by a plague of hungry locusts. Finally the whole country (apart from the part where the Israelites lived) was plunged into darkness for three full days. And *still* Pharaoh's heart was hard as nails.

When the word came that he had sent Moses packing for the tenth time, the Israelite leaders were summoned to a special meeting. What would happen now? Back at home, Deborah and Benji waited with bated breath. Pharaoh's hardness of heart was like a huge wall, blocking their path to freedom, but they were sure God wouldn't let it stand in their way for ever.

'If there's one thing these last few months have shown me, it's just how great and powerful God is,' observed Deborah, as they sat around the fire. 'And from the look on Miriam's face, I think she feels the same way – only I never get the chance to speak to her, because Jake's always dragging her off on some new money-making scheme.'

At the mention of Jake's name, her brother rolled his eyes. They certainly knew now what he meant about making the most of things. During the plague of blood he'd dug up fresh water and sold it by the cupful to thirsty Egyptians. Then he'd worked as a frog-catcher during the plague of frogs. He'd sold fly-swats during the plague of flies and fresh fruit and vegetables after the plagues of hail and locusts. Now, after the plague of darkness, he was dealing in candles and oil lamps.

'He's made enough money to buy a new house – or so he says. But what good is a house in Egypt when God's giving us a whole new land of our own?' Benji marvelled.

'I suppose he just doesn't believe that's going to happen,' said Deborah.

'He's got no faith – that's his problem,' agreed Benji.

As Benji spoke, the door opened and the children's father strode into the room. From the solemn expression on his face, it was clear there had been a major development.

'God is going to send one last plague – the worst yet,' he announced. 'It will mean deaths, I'm afraid. But if we follow his instructions, we'll be safe.'

No sooner were the words out of his mouth than the door opened again and Miriam appeared in the doorway.

'Deborah, can I speak to you for a moment?'

'Of course,' said Deborah. She was on her feet and across the room in an instant to find out what Miriam wanted.

'It . . . it's Jake,' Miriam stammered. 'He met some Egyptian merchants yesterday. They promised him a bag of gold if he could stop the plagues. And now he's gone.'

'Gone!' Deborah frowned. 'You mean gone to see Pharaoh!'

'No!' Miriam dropped her voice to a whisper. 'Gone to steal Moses' staff. He thinks that without that staff, Moses won't have any power.'

Deborah's jaw dropped.

'I know what you're thinking,' Miriam went on miserably. 'Jake's a traitor, and now he's going to ruin everything.'

'No it's not that,' Deborah assured her. 'Moses' power comes from God. Stealing his staff won't make any difference.'

'Oh Deborah! Do you really think so?' For a moment Miriam looked relieved. 'I wouldn't want a brother of mine to wreck our chance of freedom.' Then her face clouded over. 'But what will happen to him?'

'I don't know,' said Deborah.

Deep down, though, she was worried. She didn't want to scare her friend, but she felt sure that Jake was in danger – very great danger indeed.

Teaching point

We experience God's power when we act in faith.

Bible reading

Matthew 9:20–22. The background to this story is found in Exodus 7–10.

Application

Ask the group to think of some natural sources of power and energy and give some facts about their effects, e.g. if all the energy from one hurricane in a single day could be converted into electricity, it would be enough to supply the whole of the USA for three years. Then say that the greatest source of natural power and energy we can think of is nothing compared to the power of God. But in order to experience God's power we need to have faith. Aim to bring out the point that there are two aspects to having faith: (a) believing something about God, and (b) being ready to act on that belief. In this week's story Jake does not have faith in God, and so he acts in one way, while Deborah and Benji, who do have faith, act in another.

Read Matthew 9:20–22 (the healing of the woman who touched the hem of Jesus' robe). Here was a woman who had been imprisoned by illness for twelve years. She had 'active' faith that Jesus could help her – and he did. Remind the group how powerful God is – that he is able to do anything; he is bigger than the biggest problem. Point out that we experience God's power on the road to freedom when we act in faith.

Songs

Be bold, be strong, for the Lord your God is with you
    (SOFK 6, JP 14)
God is our guide, our light and our deliverer (JP 56)
How great is our God! How great is His name! (JP 82)
In the stars His handiwork I see (JP 112)
My faith is like a staff of oak (JP 168)
My God is so big, so strong and so mighty (SOFK 134,
    JP 169)
My Lord is higher than a mountain (JP 170)
When Israel was in Egypt's land (JP 276)
I'm going to take a step of faith (JP 381)
Mighty is our God (JP 431)
O Lord, You're great, You are fabulous (SOFK 143,
    JP 435)

33. Part Five: Free at Last

At that moment Jake was in the market-place. *He* certainly didn't feel he was in danger. All he cared about was getting Moses' staff, and he had a simple plan to get it. He knew Moses would pass through the market-place on his way home after meeting with the Israelite elders. His plan was to leap out from among the stalls as the old man went by and snatch the staff from his grasp.

As he expected, before long there was a bit of a flurry at the end of the street and the Israelite leader appeared. Jake's eyes narrowed, intent on the thin curved piece of wood in the old man's hand. He tensed up, ready to make a grab for it. And then, just as he was about to dive forward, Moses turned aside.

Where was he going? The boy stepped out into the main thoroughfare, only to see Moses walk over to the carpenter's stall. Crippled camels! Jake's mouth dropped in amazement. The Israelite leader had just bought a brand new staff. What's more, he was tossing his old staff aside – which could only mean one thing: that staff wasn't the source of his power.

After what he'd just seen Jake couldn't slip back into the shadows. It was as if the carpenter's stall was drawing him like a magnet. Next thing he knew, he and the Israelite leader were face to face.

'We've met before, haven't we?' said Moses.

'Er . . . yes . . .' Jake swayed slightly.

'Steady on there. Are you feeling all right?'

'It's . . . er . . . nothing. I've just had a bit of a shock.'

'Carpenter!' Moses called over his shoulder. 'Give this lad here my old staff. We've a long hot journey ahead of us, and even an old staff is better than nothing.'

Then he squeezed Jake's shoulder in a fatherly manner and continued on his way.

Meanwhile in Israelite homes throughout Egypt, the heads of families were passing on the instructions they'd been given at the meeting. 'We're to pack up our things and keep on our outdoor clothes,' they were telling their wives and children. 'We aren't going to bed tonight. Instead every family group is to prepare a special meal of roast lamb. Most important of all, we have to make a mark with the lamb's blood on our front doors.'

Everyone knew that something major was about to happen.

'I have the same sort of life-and-death feeling as I had the night Nathan was born,' Deborah told Benji.

Benji nodded. He felt that solemn feeling too – especially when Simeon brought in the body of the lamb, took a blood-soaked cloth and made the mark on their door.

Soon the house was full of the smell of roast meat. The children ate their fill and relaxed with their parents in the warmth of the fire. The hours crept past. Deborah's eyes grew heavy. 'Mustn't . . . fall . . . asleep. Mustn't . . . fall. . . .'

'Let's have a sing-song,' suggested Benji, seeing her yawns.

'Good idea,' said Simeon, and the sing-song got underway with each family member taking it in turns to choose a favourite song. And then, at four o'clock in the morning, a very unexpected caller brought the hours of waiting to an end.

It was the children's mother's Egyptian mistress. She was at the door looking quite unlike her usual immaculate self, with her hair loosely tied back, and no make-up. 'Pharaoh wants you and your people to leave Egypt at once,' she told Simeon breathlessly. 'Here are some goodbye gifts.' She turned on her heel and disappeared off into the darkness, leaving Simeon holding four fleecy cloaks and a jewellery box.

Now their door was open, the children could see that the street outside was full of activity. They heard footsteps, voices, the braying of a donkey. 'This is it!' Simeon turned to them with a triumphant smile. 'There are Egyptians calling at every Israelite home, begging us to go. . . .'

'You mean . . . you mean we're actually *leaving*?' Deborah squeaked.

'Yes,' Simeon nodded. 'We're free.'

Of course there was still one very big question. Why had Pharaoh finally changed his mind? It wasn't until they were out in the street with all their belongings that Deborah and Benji heard the answer. Apparently that night, while they'd been sitting around the fire, the tenth plague had struck. 'At midnight the eldest son in every Egyptian home died,' Simeon told them soberly. 'The only homes where the sons escaped death were the ones with blood on the door.'

The sun rose. It was their first day of freedom, but all

Deborah and Benji could think about was Jake. Miriam had said her brother had planned to spend the night with some Egyptian friends.

'He's an eldest son. If he didn't go home last night. . . .' Deborah stopped.

'He'd have been caught in the plague,' finished Benji. 'It's awful. I mean, I know he brought it on himself, but I can't help wondering . . . if only we'd made more of an effort to talk to him. . . .'

Suddenly his sister caught his arm. 'Look! Am I seeing things, or is that Jake – up there with Miriam at the top of the street?'

Benji screwed up his eyes. Then he gave a yell of delight: 'That's him all right. Come on!'

Within a couple of minutes the four children were together.

Jake didn't waste any time on small-talk. 'You don't have to tell me,' he announced before either Benji or Deborah could say a word. 'I messed up big time, and nearly paid for it with my life.' He paused and then added quietly, 'Late last night I decided not to stay with my Egyptian mates after all. I got home just before midnight.'

'Phew! That was close!' breathed Benji. 'So how come you saw sense?'

'It was something that happened in the market-place earlier in the day,' Jake said slowly. 'Something that made me realise how real God was. I felt terrible at first, thinking of the stupid things I'd said and done. But coming in through the door last night, I prayed he would forgive me.'

There was a moment of silence as the four children remembered the awesome events of the previous night.

'God has forgiven you, Jake,' said Deborah softly. 'It's a new beginning – for all of us.'

'Sure thing,' agreed Benji. 'This is the greatest adventure of our lives, and we're in it together.'

'It will be cold in the desert at nights,' observed practical Miriam. 'But the Egyptians have given us plenty of warm cloaks.'

'And jewels,' added Deborah.

'And Moses gave me his staff,' Jake piped up.

There was a brief moment of silence.

'Gave you his staff! When? Why?' the others cried.

Their friend looked mysterious. Jake had changed a lot, but he still enjoyed teasing. 'That's for me to know and you to find out,' he grinned.

Teaching point

Accepting God's offer of freedom and forgiveness.

Bible reading

Luke 13:22–30. This story is based on Exodus 11–12.

Application

After telling the story hold up pictures of an open door and a closed door. First, ask the group for some ideas they associate with an open door (opportunities, welcome, adventure, home). Do the same with the symbol of the closed door. Aim to bring out the fact that a closed door can mean either safety and inclusion, or sadness and exclusion, depending on which side you are on. The four children in the story all ended up on the right side of the door, and for them it became a gateway to freedom and adventure.

Introduce Luke 13:22–30 as a reading which shows some people ending up on the other side of the door. Read the passage and then point out that when Jesus talks about ways and gates and doors, he is actually referring to himself. For us today he is the open doorway leading to a new life of freedom and adventure. The question is, will we go through?

Songs

Cleanse me from my sin, Lord (JP 27)
'Follow Me' says Jesus (JP 46)
He made the stars to shine (JP 76)
I met You at the cross (JP 103)
In my need Jesus found me (JP 109)
Jesus loves me! This I know (JP 140)
Live, live, live (JP 153)
On Calvary's tree He died for me (JP 183)
There is a green hill far away (JP 245)
When Israel was in Egypt's land (JP 276)
I've come to a time when I must change (JP 383)
Sorry, Lord, for all the things (JP 463)

SEPTEMBER

Friends

34. Blaze and Dasher

Once upon a time two red deer, Blaze and Dasher, lived on a magnificent forest estate in the back of beyond. It was a beautiful place and the deer spent many happy hours racing nose to tail among the trees. Then one day Peaceful Park, as it was called, was bought by a famous film star who wanted to get away from it all. 'At the end of the week I plan to move into my new home and enjoy the peace and quiet,' she told her manager.

Immediately the manager got on the line to Boots, the Head Forester. 'Miss Shakespeare will be expecting a big welcome party when she arrives,' the manager said. 'Lay on a barbecue. Organise entertainment. Get a deer roasting on a spit.'

'Anything you say, boss!' Boots swung into action. Blaze and Dasher, meanwhile, had no idea that Peaceful Park had changed hands – until suddenly disaster struck. There they were racing nose to tail among the trees when the ground seemed to open up under their hooves. Next thing they knew they were tumbling downwards. They had been caught in a trap.

A few hours later a landrover pulled up beside them, and Boots got out.

'Oh good!' he said. He seemed very relieved to find the trap full. 'Two deer. That should be more than enough.' He bundled Blaze and Dasher into a trailer and drove them to the castle at the heart of the estate, where he shut them up in a wooden pen on the lawn.

The two deer looked around, amazed at the sight of humans running to and fro carrying all sorts of strange-looking objects. 'What's going on?' they asked a chatty sparrow.

'Our park has been bought by Sally Shakespeare, the film star,' the sparrow told them. 'There's going to be a posh bar-becue in her honour.'

Then it winked in the direction of the marquee which sat like a gigantic mushroom on the grass. 'That's the big tent, where her guests are going to dance.' It fluttered over to a table full of shimmering things that sparkled like sunlit water. 'These are glasses,' it chirped, 'for her guests to drink out of.' It hopped across some slender things that gleamed like silver fish. 'Knives and forks,' it cheeped, 'for her guests to eat with.' Finally it pecked round a heap of small black stones piled up on the ground. 'Charcoal,' said the sparrow, 'for barbecuing the. . . .' It stopped.

'For barbecuing the what?' asked Blaze.

'Oh never mind!' The sparrow flew off leaving Blaze and Dasher wide-eyed with dismay. They weren't stupid. They could guess what the bird had been about to say. The reason they'd been brought to this barbecue was because roast deer was on the menu.

'Oh Blaze, I'm scared,' said Dasher.

'Don't think about it,' whispered Blaze. 'Close your eyes and imagine we're back in the forest.'

'I can't! I can't!' whimpered Dasher.

And neither could Blaze. For Boots had just walked over to the pen accompanied by a butcher, armed with a long sharp knife.

'There's no point in butchering more animals than we need,' the butcher said. 'One deer should be enough.'

'Right,' said Boots. 'Which one do you want to kill?'

The deer stared at each other, scarcely able to believe what they'd heard. One of them would live and the other would die.

And suddenly Blaze saw a way of saving his friend. He lifted one of his hind legs off the ground and limped across the pen, pretending to be lame.

'Look! The one with the white stripe has gone lame,' the butcher pointed out.

'Well that settles it,' shrugged Boots. 'There's no point in freeing an injured deer. It's funny though. I could have sworn he wasn't limping a moment ago.'

The butcher produced a rope, and Blaze stood quite still, making it easy for him to slip the noose round his neck.

'Goodbye, my friend,' he whispered to Dasher. 'I'll. . . .'

Vrrooomm! The roar of an engine drowned his words. A big black limousine was sweeping up the drive. For a few moments everyone froze. Then '*What's going on?!*' a woman yelled at the top of her voice.

'Miss Shakespeare!' gasped Boots. 'You're early.'

'A good thing too,' the film star replied, whirling across the lawn like a hurricane in high heels. 'I come here in search of peace and quiet, and what do I find? A circus! Well let me tell you – I'm not having it. No way!'

And so just like that the barbecue was off. The marquee came down. The knives, forks and glasses were packed up.

'And while you're at it, take those cute little customers back to the forest where they belong,' Sally Shakespeare ordered.

Accordingly, within half an hour Blaze and Dasher were back racing nose to tail between the trees, marvelling at the strange human world they had left behind.

'Did you see the look on Boots' face when the woman arrived?' cried Blaze.

'No. I missed that,' said Dasher.

'Well, did you see the powerful metal monster she got out of?'

'No. I missed that too,' said Dasher.

'Well, did you see all her golden jewellery?'

''Fraid not,' said Dasher.

'Oh Dasher,' cried Blaze. 'What *did* you see?'

'Something more amazing than the woman, more powerful than the monster, and more precious than gold,' said Dasher. 'I saw a friend who was ready to lay down his life for me.'

Teaching point

In Jesus we have a friend who laid down his life for us.

Bible reading

John 15:9–17.

Application

After telling the story show the symbol of a cross and ask the group what it reminds them of (that Jesus was a friend who laid down his life for us). Say that just before he went to the cross Jesus told his disciples how he wanted them to treat their friends. Read John 15:9–17. Then point out that 'laying down our lives for our friends' is not just about being ready to die in a friend's place. It can also mean behaving unselfishly. Encourage the group to give some examples of unselfish behaviour. Finish with a prayer asking Jesus to help us follow his example of love.

Songs

God so loved the world He sent to us Jesus (JP 59)
I'm special (SOFK 92, JP 106)
It is a thing most wonderful (JP 117)
Jesus' love is very wonderful (SOFK 109, JP 139)
On Calvary's tree He died for me (JP 183)
One, two, three, Jesus loves me (JP 189)
Thank You Jesus, thank You Jesus (JP 235)
A new commandment (SOFK 4, JP 303)
Everyone in the whole wide world (JP 333)
I have a friend who is deeper than the ocean (JP 370)
Let's go and tell our friends that Jesus cares (JP 416)
Think big: an elephant (JP 479)
You can weigh an elephant's auntie (JP 501)

35. Lucy's Week

(The opening meeting of a children's club
or uniformed organisation)

Five-year-old Lucy had two special friends. Lucy's first special friend was her eight-year-old sister, Lisa. And her second special friend was a well-worn teddy, who went by the name of Best Bear. This story begins on a Monday, when a big removal van pulled up beside Lucy's front gate. Immediately she saw the van, Lucy hopped onto a flowerpot. She looked over the fence, and saw a young woman, wearing jeans and a T-shirt, walking down the next door path.

'Hello! Are you our new neighbour?' Lucy called.

'Yes,' said the woman. 'My name's Ann. Who are you?'

'I'm Lucy,' said Lucy. 'And this is Best Bear.'

Ann came over to the fence. She shook Lucy's hand and Best Bear's paw. 'Pleased to meet you,' she said.

197

The next day was Tuesday. And on Tuesday Lucy just happened to be standing on her flowerpot looking over the garden fence when Ann came out of the house. She seemed to be wearing some sort of uniform.*

'Hello, Ann,' called Lucy. 'Why are you dressed like that?'

'I'm dressed like this because I'm helping with Rainbows in the church hall,' said Ann.

'What's Rainbows?' asked Lucy.

'It's a weekly meeting for girls aged five to seven,' Ann explained.

Lucy liked the sound of this. 'If Mummy brought me to the church hall, could I join in?' she asked.

Ann said, 'Of course.'

So that Tuesday Lucy and Best Bear went to Rainbows for the first time. They did all the things that Rainbows usually do – having fun, playing games. And then, towards the end of the evening, Ann told everyone a story about the first people who ever lived. Their names were Adam and Eve. And Ann told the Rainbows how Adam and Eve had worked in a beautiful garden and had God for a special friend. But then they spoiled things by disobeying God – which meant they couldn't be his special friends any more and had to leave the garden.

As soon as Lucy heard this her hand shot up. 'Please, Ann,' she said. 'Best Bear is my special friend. And my other special friend is Lisa, my sister. And it's her birthday tomorrow.'

The next day was Wednesday. A very exciting day for Lisa. She came down for breakfast and there were two surprise parcels waiting to be opened. The first present she opened was from her mum and dad. It was a computer. Wow! The second present was from Lucy. It was a bit of a mystery. Lisa held it this way and that way, but she couldn't work out what it was.

'It's a postman's hat, silly,' said Lucy. 'I made it so you could put it on your head and pretend to be Postman Pat.'

'That's brilliant, Lucy!' cried Lisa. 'I've got a computer from mum and dad, and a postman's hat from Lucy. This is my best birthday ever.'

The next day was Thursday. And on Thursday Lucy had a special favour to ask Lisa. 'Please can I play in your bedroom straight away after school?'

Now Lisa was a very kind sister, and she knew that Lucy sometimes got a bit bored and lonely when she came home from school at twelve o'clock, so she said, 'Yes. You can play in my bedroom. You can play with anything you like, as long as you don't touch my computer.'

The minute Lucy got back from school she went straight into Lisa's bedroom. The postman's hat was lying on the bed, so Lucy put it on and pretended to be Postman Pat, going round the bedroom posting things. She posted some toy money into Lisa's wardrobe and she posted some tiddly-wink counters into the drawer beside the bed. And then she came to the computer. And there in the front of the computer she saw a little slot that looked exactly like a letter-box. . . .

Three hours later, when Lisa came home, she went into the bedroom straight away to play with her new computer. 'You're very quiet,' she said to Lucy. Then she pressed the ON switch and waited for the screen to spring to life. But – oh dear! – something had gone wrong. The computer wasn't working. And Lisa suddenly noticed that as well as keeping very quiet, Lucy was looking very guilty.

'You touched my computer, didn't you!' she yelled.

'It wasn't me. I didn't post toy money into it,' cried Lucy. 'It was Best Bear.'

The next day was Friday. And that Friday Lisa made it very clear that Lucy wasn't her special friend any more. Not only did she dump the postman's hat Lucy had given her in the kitchen pedal bin, she made a big sign saying: 'KEEP OUT, LUCY!' and stuck it on her bedroom door.

The big sign was still there when Lucy got up on Saturday. She couldn't go into the bedroom to play with Lisa, so she went out into the garden instead. She sat on her flowerpot, thinking back over the week, and she remembered Ann's story. 'I'm like Adam and Eve,' she thought miserably. 'I've spoiled things by doing what I was told not to.'

And suddenly it struck her that God might be able to help her put things right. So she closed her eyes tight, and said, 'Please God, help me to put things right with Lisa.'

Now sometimes when we ask God for that kind of help and really mean what we say, God answers by putting an idea of something we could do into our heads.

And that was what happened with Lucy. God gave her an idea.

She got up and went into the kitchen. For the next few minutes she was very busy wrapping something up in newspaper. Then she put on the postman's hat (which she'd fished out of the bin) and she made her way to Lisa's room. Knock! Knock! She knocked on the door. Lisa opened the door and Lucy handed her the newspaper parcel. 'It's a special delivery,' she said.

'A special delivery of what?' said Lisa in a cross voice.

'Of Best Bear,' said Lucy. 'I'm giving him to you to make up for posting toy money into your computer. I'm giving him to you so you won't be mad at me any more.'

'You've given me Best Bear!' Lisa exclaimed, really touched. She knew how much Best Bear meant to Lucy. 'I'll tell you what. I'll keep him in my room until tea-time, and then you can take him back.'

'But will keeping him until tea-time be enough to put things right?' asked Lucy anxiously.

'Yes,' said Lisa, hugging her and pulling the notice off the door.

The next day was Sunday – the day when Lucy, Lisa, their mum and Best Bear all went to church. Funnily enough, that Sunday the minister talked about putting things right. 'After Adam and Eve spoiled people's friendship with God,' he said, 'God put things right by sending his own Son Jesus to die on a cross. So today anyone – no matter who they are, or what they've done – can become God's special friend.'

Well, Lucy thought this was very good news. And that night, at bedtime, she knelt down and thanked God for what he'd done. And then she thanked him for Ann and for Rainbows and for church where she could learn more about Jesus. And then she hopped into bed and snuggled down under the duvet with Best Bear.

And that was the end of the week.

Telling this story to a group

Alternative uniformed organisations may be substituted for 'Rainbows'. If using the story with a non-uniformed children's club, adapt as follows from the asterisk:

She was carrying a box of bats and balls.
'Hello, Ann,' called Lucy. 'Where are you taking that box?'
'I'm taking it to the church hall for the _____ Club.'
'What's that?' asked Lucy.

To use the story with a boys' organisation/club, change the sex of the central characters.

Teaching point

Through Jesus, God can be a special friend to us – a friend who is with us every day of every week.

Bible reading

Deuteronomy 31:8.

Application

After telling the story show the group a calendar. Ask if they
can remember what day of the week Lucy went to Rainbows
(Tuesday). Ask which day of the week was the most exciting
day for Lisa (Wednesday – her birthday). Then remind the
group that Friday was a bad day for Lucy – a day when Lisa
wouldn't speak to her or play with her. But Saturday was a
good day – a day when God helped her put things right. Say
that the weeks of our lives are made up of good days and bad
days, ordinary days and exciting days, but that whatever kind
of day it is, God wants us to remember he is with us (read
Deuteronomy 31:8), and he wants us to enjoy the special
friendship which we can have with him through Jesus.

Songs

God so loved the world He sent to us Jesus (JP 59)
I'm special (SOFK 92, JP 106)
Jesus is a friend of mine (JP 136)
The steadfast love of the Lord never ceases (JP 250)
What a friend we have in Jesus (JP 273)
What a wonderful Saviour is Jesus (JP 274)
All you have to do is ask the Lord (JP 307)
Did you ever talk to God above (JP 329)
Everyone in the whole wide world (JP 333)
I have a friend who is deeper than the ocean (JP 370)

36. Operation Skylight

Jesus of Nazareth had come to town, and Capernaum was buzzing with the news. Women talked about him at the well. Shoppers talked about him in the market-place. 'He's amazing! He casts out demons and heals the sick,' they said.

Four lads – Zac, Johnny, Philip and Mark – pricked up their ears when they heard that. They had a friend who was sick. Once Dan had larked about with them after synagogue school. But these days he lay helplessly on a thin mattress in his parents' home, unable to move his legs.

'Do you think Jesus could help Dan?' Zac wondered.

'There's only one way to find out,' said Johnny.

And that was how Operation Skylight began – with the four lads going round to Dan's house, where they trooped in just as a familiar figure from synagogue school marched out.

'Out of my way, boys. I'm in a hurry,' the teacher said as he pushed past, robes flapping out behind.

'As if Dan didn't have enough problems!' shrugged Philip. 'Every time Rabbi Obed drops by he tells him he's paralysed because of all the bad things he's done. No wonder the guy feels guilty!'

They found their friend lying on his mat as usual, staring up at the ceiling.

'Hiya, Dan. How are things?' Zac asked, trying his best to sound cheerful, though the gloomy look on Dan's face had already given him an answer.

'I've been thinking about all the times I broke God's law,' Dan sighed. 'The lies I told, the times I didn't obey my mum and dad. Rabbi Obed is right. I can't move and it's all my own fault.'

The boys looked at each other and got straight to the point. 'We're here to tell you that the great teacher and healer, Jesus of Nazareth, is in Capernaum.'

'I know,' Dan said, keeping his eyes on the ceiling. 'Rabbi Obed has gone round to the house where he's staying.'

'So how about us taking you round to the house too?' said Zac.

'Go on. He might be able to help you, Dan,' the others urged.

'All right,' Dan sighed. 'I suppose I've nothing to lose.'

The boys had thought it would all be plain sailing (or rather, plain carrying) after that. What they hadn't bargained for was arriving at the house, only to find themselves as the tail end of an elephant-sized queue. By the look of things, half the population of Capernaum had come to see Jesus that morning.

'Forget it, guys. This isn't going to work,' Dan muttered. 'You might as well just carry me back home.'

But Zac and Co hadn't carted their friend up and down streets for half an hour in the blazing sun for nothing.

'How about shouting "fire!" and waiting for everyone to run away?' suggested Philip.

'How about forming ourselves into a sort of human battering ram and forcing our way in?' That was Mark.

'How about asking God for help?' said Johnny, closing his eyes.

The first thing he spotted when he opened them again was a coil of rope, lying at the bottom of the outside steps which led up to the flat roof of the house. 'Hey, wait a minute!' The rope gave him an idea – a *much* better idea than anything suggested so far.

'We could make a hole in the roof,' he cried.

Now what you've got to understand here is that in those days making holes in roofs was no big deal. It was simply a matter of digging down through the packing of twigs and mud between the beams, which didn't take the lads long. In a matter of minutes they were ready to lower their friend through the hole.

'Hold tight, Dan! Easy does it!' Carefully they let the ropes out – longer and longer – until finally the earth floor took the weight. Eagerly the four peered down into the room below. They saw a large number of astonished onlookers brushing fallen twigs from their robes. And – yes! – there was Jesus, with Dan, bang on target, at his feet.

To the boys' relief, the great teacher didn't seem in the least bit put out. Quite the opposite. He was actually smiling – a reassuring 'thanks-fellas-you've-done-your-bit-now-I'll-do-mine' type of smile. Then he turned back to Dan and said gently, 'Son, your sins are forgiven.'

Amazing! Zac saw Dan's whole face brighten at the words. But they didn't go down well with Rabbi Obed and his fellow scribes. If looks could have killed, Jesus would have been dead on the spot! 'How dare you! Only God can forgive sins!' those looks said.

To the end of their days the boys never forgot what happened next. Jesus faced the religious know-alls – those men who had done nothing for Dan except tell him he was sick because of his sin. 'Which do you think is easier to say?' he asked calmly. '"Son, your sins are forgiven," or "Son, get up, take your mat and walk"?' And while they were still groping for an answer, he smiled over at Dan and said, 'Get up, take your mat and walk.'

And Dan did. Slowly, but without the slightest hesitation, he sat up, then stood up, then took a step and then another . . . and another . . . and another. . . .

The crowd went wild. '*He's walking*! Praise God! Praise God!' they yelled.

'*He's walking*!' The four friends hugged one another joyfully.

'He's *walking*?' The teachers of religion swallowed hard. If the paralysed lad was walking that meant he must have been healed. If he'd been healed, he must have been forgiven. If he'd been forgiven, it must have been by Jesus. But only *God* could forgive sins. . . .

'Just look at Rabbi Obed's face!' laughed Zac.

'Never mind Rabbi Obed,' cried Johnny. 'We'll have to hurry to catch up with Dan.'

But Zac caught him by the tunic. 'Hang on a minute!'

'What for?' Johnny looked puzzled. 'Oh yeah. I get it.' He rolled up his sleeves. 'First we've got to fix this hole in the roof.'

Teaching point

The paralysed man had true friends – friends ready to do everything they could to bring him to Jesus.

Bible reading

This story is based on Mark 2:1–11.

Application

After telling the story hold up the proverb 'A friend in need is a friend indeed' and ask the group what this means (a real friend will be there for you when things go wrong). Point out that Johnny, Zac and Co were real friends to Dan when things went wrong in his life. Ask for some examples of things that can go wrong for our friends (e.g. sickness, problems at home, disappointments). Then ask for suggestions of ways we can help them. Aim to bring out the fact that, just like the lads in the story, we can bring them to Jesus – not physically, but through praying for them and showing them his love.

Songs

Come to Jesus, 'He's amazing' (JP 33)
God forgave my sin in Jesus' name (SOFK 37, JP 54)
Go, tell it on the mountain (JP 65)
There's a new life in Jesus (JP 249)
Everyone in the whole wide world (JP 333)
God loves you and I love you (SOFK 42, JP 348)
Let's go and tell our friends that Jesus cares (JP 416)
Once there was a house, a busy little house (SOFK 144, JP 444)

37. The Making of a Hero

(A true story from the life of André Trocmé)

This is a story about a French boy called André – a boy who grew up to be a hero. He was a hero because during the Second World War he risked his own life saving the lives of hundreds of Jews. But it was years earlier, during the First World War, that the seeds were sown that led him to act so bravely.

As a child, André was quite lonely. Instead of going to school, he had his own teachers coming to teach him, and instead of playing in the streets with the local children, he played in a beautiful garden surrounded by a high stone wall. Then came the First World War and everything changed. The French city where his family lived was invaded by the German army. German troops even took over part of their home. Suddenly André's sheltered life became quite different. There were terrible food shortages. For the first time the boy knew what it felt like to be hungry. But he also learned, for the first time, what it felt like to have friends.

André's friends were a group of young people who used to meet every week in a bare old room above the church. There they shared their ups and downs, their hopes and fears. They would read the Bible together and pray for each other. Their closeness was built on their faith in God and their desire to help people worse off than themselves.

Some people who clearly needed help were the prisoners in a nearby prison camp. André and his friends might be short of food, but these men were starving. So, every day, the young people would slip into the camps with a big pot full of vegetables. And every day, as they slipped back out again, they would tell each other how much they hated the Germans.

Then, one afternoon, back inside his own home André bumped into a German soldier on the staircase. There was nothing unusual in this since German soldiers were still occupying the house. What was unusual was the fact that this soldier stopped and offered the boy a thick slice of black potato bread.

'Are you hungry?' he asked.

'No,' said André sharply. 'And even if I was hungry I wouldn't take bread from you because you are my enemy.'

The German soldier put his bread back in his pocket. 'I am not what you think,' he said quietly. 'I am a Christian.' Then he explained that his name was Kindler and that since joining the army he had given his life to Christ. 'My job is sending telegrams,' he went on. 'But I am often in danger when I am out on the battlefield. Still, I don't carry a gun or a bayonet. I just sing a hymn and pray to God.'

André looked Kindler up and down, struggling to make sense of this.

'My friends and I sing hymns and pray to God,' he said slowly. 'You can come to one of our meetings if you like.'

So the next Sunday André brought Kindler to the church hall to meet his friends.

At the first sight of the German soldier a wave of fear ran through the group. Were they about to be arrested?

'Don't worry,' André reassured them. 'Kindler is a Christian just like us and he's here to worship God.'

Knowing how much his friends hated Germans, the boy was taking a risk. But it was all right. As soon as the young people heard that Kindler was a Christian, they smiled and offered him a seat.

The service that evening was a service with a difference. Kindler's German accent could be clearly heard, joining in the hymns and prayers.

'Perhaps our visitor would like to speak to us,' someone suggested at the end of the meeting.

'Certainly.' The soldier got up, and in the straightforward sincere way that had so impressed André, he told the story of how he had come to Christ. He finished by encouraging the young people to follow their Saviour's example of love. 'Jesus taught us to love our enemies,' he said simply. 'That is his good news. We should help, not hurt each other.'

By the time Kindler had stopped speaking, there was such a sense of God's presence in the hall that the whole group were on their knees. What's more, the seed had been sown that would later inspire André to save so many lives. Thanks to Kindler, he stopped dividing the world into friends and enemies. All human beings, he saw, were precious to God.

Teaching point

Loving our enemies.

Bible reading

Matthew 5:43–48.

Application

It is probably best to let this story do its own work. After telling it, simply read Matthew 5:43–48 – the passage on which Kindler based his message. Finish by praying for people in other parts of the world, particularly those in war-torn situations.

Extra information

André Pascal Trocmé (1901–71) was born in the city of Saint-Quentin in north-eastern France. During the Second World War he was a Protestant pastor in the village of Le Chambon-sur-Lignon.

The source of this story is *Lest Innocent Blood Be Shed – The Story of the Village of Le Chambon and How Goodness Happened There* by Philip Hallie (HarperCollins, 1994).

Songs

God forgave my sin in Jesus' name (SOFK 37, JP 54)
God so loved the world He sent us Jesus (JP 59)
Go, tell it on the mountain (JP 65)
Jesus died for all the children (JP 132)
Make me a channel of your peace (SOFK 130, JP 161)
Thank You for ev'ry new good morning (JP 230)
When I needed a neighbour (JP 275)
Jesus, send me the helper (JP 409)

OCTOBER

Food and Harvest

38. Ready, Steady, Cook!

In the Middle Ages a man called St Francis of Assisi served Christ by travelling from village to village, preaching and praying. His followers were known as Franciscan friars. Like their leader, they lived out their faith in a simple way. They wore plain brown robes called habits and lived together in simple little homes called friaries.

One day the Franciscan friars in a certain friary welcomed a special visitor under their roof. His name was Brother Juniper. He was one of St Francis' closest companions, and he was so generous he once let a beggar take the habit from his back.

As well as being very generous, Brother Juniper was a man of prayer. He loved to talk to God, and when he started praying, he would keep going for hours.

Now it so happened that a few days after Brother Juniper came to the friary, the rest of the friars had to go out. 'Brother Juniper, could you please prepare the evening meal while we're gone,' the head friar said.

'Leave it to me,' Brother Juniper said gladly, for as well as being very generous and very prayerful, he was always very willing to help. Still he couldn't help thinking that time was much better spent praying than cooking – so he hit on an idea. 'I know,' he thought. 'Since I am here to cook, I'll prepare so much food that the friars won't have to interrupt their prayers to cook again for a whole fortnight.'

Then he thought of all the things he would need – cooking pots, fresh meat, salted meat, chickens, eggs, cabbage, tomatoes – and he set off into town to beg for them. An hour later he was back. Mission accomplished! The great cook-in was about to begin.

Unfortunately, Brother Juniper had never cooked before, but that didn't hold him back. He lit a huge fire, filled all his pots with water and put them on to boil. When the water was boiling, he tossed the ingredients into the pots. In they all went – whole cabbages, eggs with their shells on and chickens complete with feathers and feet. Soon the fire was giving off such a fierce heat that the friar had to wear a wooden board like an apron to stop himself getting scorched. It was heavy and awkward, but he hopped cheerfully backwards and forwards between the pots, stirring first one, then another, until finally the food was ready to serve.

By this time the other friars were home and waiting hungrily in the dining-room.

What a surprise they got when instead of coming in with one small pot, their cook produced six very large ones. 'It's stew,' he told them happily. And indeed they needed to be told what it was, for no one had ever seen such a mixture.

'Eat your dinner and then let's go and pray,' Brother Juniper said as he dished it up. 'And by the way, no one need work in the kitchen for the next fortnight, because there's enough stew here to keep us going for two whole weeks.'

For a few moments the friars sat in stunned silence, staring at the hotch-potch on their plates, taking in the feathers and the chicken beaks and the bits of claw and shell.

'Eat up! It will do you good!' Brother Juniper kept telling them.

At last the head friar found his voice: 'Do us good? What can you be thinking of, Brother Juniper? It's disgusting.'

Now most cooks would be deeply offended if someone said that about a meal they'd prepared. But as well as being generous and prayerful and willing to help, Brother Juniper was a very hard man to offend.

So now he took a mouthful of his stew and chewed it slowly. Then he screwed up his face and plucked a feather from his teeth. 'You're right,' he said sadly. 'It *is* disgusting! And I deserve to be whipped for such a waste.'

Of course the friars wouldn't hear of any punishment. They might be going to bed hungry, but in a funny way Brother Juniper *had* done them good.

'We wish we were all as generous, prayerful, helpful and ready to own up to our mistakes as you are, dear brother,' the head friar said. 'So please, don't get into a stew about your cooking.'

Teaching point

The growth of Christian character.

Bible reading

2 Peter 1:5–8.

Application

After telling the story hold up a recipe book. Ask the group what Brother Juniper could have learned from a recipe book that would have helped him to make a better stew (list of ingredients and method of using them). Point out that Brother Juniper didn't know what made a good stew, but he did know what makes a good Christian character. It's a recipe we find in 2 Peter 1:5–8. Read the Bible passage. Point out that verses 5 to 7 give a list of the ingredients: faith, goodness, knowledge, self-control, perseverance, godliness, kindness and love, while verse 8 gives the method: keep adding more and more!

Songs

In our work and in our play (JP 108)
I sing a song of the saints of God (JP 115)
I want to walk with Jesus Christ (SOFK 100, JP 124)
Love, joy, peace and patience, kindness (JP 158)
Make me a servant, humble and meek (JP 162)
May the mind of Christ my Saviour (JP 165)
Are you humbly grateful (JP 309)
Be holy in all that you do (JP 314)
It's the little things that show our love for Jesus (JP 403)
The most important thing for us as Christians (JP 470)

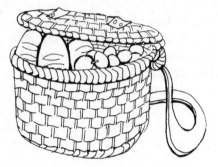

39. Rumble ... Rumble ... Hallelujah!

It's lunch-time. The disciples, passing through Samaria on their way to Galilee, have just bought some food from a village market. What a chore! They hate shopping in Samaria. They're Jews. Jews don't like Samaritans, and Samaritans don't like Jews. It's been that way for as long as anyone can remember. But at least their picnic basket is full. Rumble, rumble goes Peter's tummy. He looks inside and sees barley loaves, grapes, figs and – oh goody! – his favourite pickled olives.

By this time they have reached the top of a hill.

'Oh no!' groans James. 'Do you see what I see?' Half an hour earlier, they'd left Jesus at the bottom of the hill, all alone by a well. But he isn't alone any longer.

218

'He's talking to a Samaritan woman,' says Peter, very cross that the master is being disturbed.

Fortunately the blue-robed figure moves away as they arrive on the scene – heading in the direction of the village. 'Thank goodness for that!' Peter catches a faint whiff of her perfume as she passes. He marches over to where Jesus is sitting and announces, 'Lunch is served. We've got pickled olives and figs and barley loaves and grapes.' He starts to unpack the basket at his feet.

For a moment Jesus watches him in silence. Then he gets up. 'I don't want anything to eat, thanks,' he says, and walks away.

Not want anything! Peter is stunned. Now what? What are twelve hungry disciples meant to do when their master won't join them for lunch? Sit down and carry on without him? No, that doesn't seem right. Carefully, Peter selects the largest roll and the juiciest fig from the basket.

'We must see to it that the master keeps his strength up,' he tells the others.

So the disciples follow Jesus to the other side of the well.

'Master, eat something,' they urge.

Jesus looks thoughtfully at the crisp brown roll and the purple fig in Peter's outstretched hand. 'I have food to eat that you know nothing about,' he says.

What? The disciples frown and scratch their heads. 'Has somebody fed him? The woman perhaps?' whispers Andrew.

Peter shrugs. Knowing Jesus, the answer won't be that simple.

Rumble, rumble goes Peter's tummy. 'I want my lunch,' he thinks. 'I don't want a spiritual puzzle. I need food to give me strength.'

'*My* food is to do the will of God and to finish his work,' says Jesus.

All right, all right! Peter gets the message. Jesus is saying that real satisfaction doesn't come from eating. It comes from doing what God wants you to do.

'But God doesn't want us to do anything in *Samaria*,' he thinks.

And then he sees the teasing you're-in-for-a-surprise sort of look on Jesus' face. He hears his master say something about a harvest.

The disciple turns round. And – thundering fig leaves! – here *is* a surprise. A crowd of Samaritans are hurrying down the track towards them – a crowd led by the woman in blue. 'That's him,' she's saying, pointing to Jesus. 'There's the man I told you about – the Saviour – the Messiah, sent from God.'

From that moment lunch is the last thing on anyone's mind. Jesus is too busy teaching. The disciples are too busy helping. And the Samaritans are too busy hearing and believing. In the middle of it all, Jesus looks over at Peter and winks. Who said God had nothing for them to do here?

And Peter winks back, with a real, deep, satisfied feeling. God had given them a harvest – a big, ripe harvest of Samaritans. Rumble . . . rumble . . . hallelujah! The joy of pickled olives is nothing to this.

Teaching point

Real satisfaction comes from doing what God wants us to do.

Bible reading

This story is based on John 4:1–42.

Application

After telling the story show the group the food you most like to eat, and get examples of their favourite foods. Aim to bring out the fact that some foods become instant favourites, but with others it may take a while for us to discover how much satisfaction they give. Then say that in the story Peter discovered something that gave him more joy than his favourite food. What was it? (Doing God's will.) Finish by saying that this is a discovery God wants all of us to make.

Songs

A boy gave Jesus five loaves and two fish (JP 1)
Big man (SOFK 9, JP 16)
By blue Galilee Jesus walked of old (JP 23)
He brought me to His banqueting house (JP 73)
I'm feeding on the living bread (JP 104)
Seek ye first (SOFK 154, JP 215)
The fields are white unto harvest time (JP 237)
Have you got an appetite? (SOFK 52, JP 357)
I'm going to set my heart (JP 382)
The most important thing for us as Christians (JP 470)
We're following Jesus (JP 487)

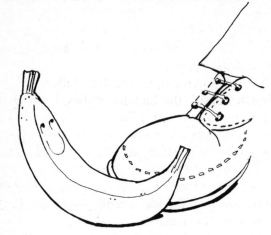

40. *Fruit in Action*

(Harvest Thanksgiving)

Imagine a beautifully decorated church. There are flower arrangements under the stained-glass windows, a magnificent display of vegetables in the front porch and a row of rosy apples on the organ. Everything looks perfect; not a caterpillar among the cabbages, not a petal out of place – except for one little detail. On top of the big black Bible in the pulpit there's a banana, sound asleep and snoring loudly.

The banana has been out for the count all weekend, and now the pulpit Bible is starting to panic. It's Sunday morning – the morning of the harvest service. And a snoring decoration could ruin everything.

'Wake up! Wake up, Banana,' it calls.

'Zzzzzzzzz,' the banana snores on.

'Oh, this is dreadful,' mutters the Bible. 'What am I to do?'
Then it remembers the Revd Oddly's special word for
making sleepy parishioners sit up in their pews. 'AMEN!' it
shouts. 'AMEN!'

This does the trick.

'What . . . when . . . where am I?' the banana stammers as
it wakes up with a jump.

'You're in a church pulpit,' the Bible tells it.

'A church pulpit!' the banana replies, looking stunned.
'The last thing I remember, I was knocking around a school
lunch-box. And now I'm in a church pulpit, you say. So
what's going on? Why am I here?'

The Bible gives the banana the run-down on harvest services. 'They happen at this time every year,' it explains. 'The
ladies put flowers on the windowsills, vegetables in the front
porch, apples on the organ. . . .'

'And a banana in the pulpit,' the banana finishes.

'Well, no actually,' the Bible sighs. 'I've never had to share
my pulpit with a banana before. I'm not sure how you got
here.'

'You mean I'm here by mistake!' yells the banana.

'It will be a very big mistake if you keep yelling like that,'
warns the Bible. 'The congregation is arriving. The harvest
service is about to begin.'

The banana wriggles forward for a better view of the
church. 'How come all the front seats are empty?' it asks.
'Does the minister bite?'

'Shhhh . . . of course not.'

The Revd Oddly walks up the aisle.

'Wow!' gasps the banana. 'He's wearing a frock!'

'It's not a frock. Those are his robes,' the Bible hisses.
'Now you really must be quiet.'

To the Bible's relief, the banana says nothing during the
opening hymn. But the moment the Revd Oddly calls the
children forward, the questions start up again.

'Why are all those kids coming to the front?' the banana wants to know.

'They're coming so the Revd Oddly can talk to them,' the Bible whispers.

'Talk to them about what?'

'Shhh. You'll have to listen and find out.'

'Boys and girls,' begins the Revd Oddly. 'This morning I want to talk to you about the fruit of the Spirit.'

'Hey! Did you hear that?' The banana leaps with excitement. 'He's talking about me.'

'No he isn't,' says the Bible.

'Yes he is. I'm fruit, aren't I?'

Before the Bible can answer, two of the children drop their collection money. And several more drum their heels against the back of the pew.

'Those kids won't learn much if they don't listen,' the banana points out. 'By the look of things the Reverend needs help to grab their attention. I know! I'll throw myself over the edge of the pulpit.'

'No! Wait! Come back, Banana,' the Bible cries.

But it's too late. The banana has flung itself forward. Next moment it's hurtling through the air.

Plonk! It narrowly misses the Revd Oddly's head and lands at his feet.

'Well I never!' he says, picking it up. 'Where did this come from?'

'From the pulpit,' the children tell him.

'Amazing! Where was I . . .?' Automatically the Revd Oddly sticks the banana into a pocket in his robes. But before he can take up where he left off, one of the children – a small girl with a long pig-tail – starts to cry.

Her big sister waves her hand in the air. 'Please, Mr Oddly. Sarah wants you to put the banana back,' she calls. 'She saved it out of her lunch-box on Friday to give to God.'

Thoughtfully the Revd Oddly takes the banana out of his

pocket. 'Did you hear that, boys and girls?' He holds it up in the air. 'Sarah really likes bananas, but she saved this one out of her lunch-box to give to God. I think that's great.'

He has the children's attention now. They listen closely as he tells them that the greatest thing about Sarah's gift was the love that made her give it. 'When the Holy Spirit puts God's love and joy and peace in our hearts, that's the fruit of the Spirit,' he says.

'And when a banana leaps from the pulpit to help the minister make a point, that's fruit in action,' the banana yells.

Teaching point

The Holy Spirit produces spiritual fruit in our lives.

Bible reading

Galatians 5:22–26.

Application

After the story show the group some different types of fruit and ask where they come from (e.g. apples from an apple tree, grapes from a vine). Say that in Galatians 5:22–26 the Bible talks about different kinds of spiritual fruit. Read the passage. Then ask the group where this spiritual fruit comes from. Aim to bring out the fact that we can't produce it ourselves; it is the result of God's Holy Spirit at work in our lives.

Songs

I've got peace like a river (JP 120)
I've got that joy, joy, joy, joy (JP 121)
Love, joy, peace and patience, kindness (JP 158)

Make me a channel of Your peace (SOFK 130, JP 161)
Someone's brought a loaf of bread (JP 220)
At harvest time we celebrate (JP 311)
It's the little things that show our love for Jesus (JP 403)
Jesus, send me the helper (JP 409)
Love, joy, peace (JP 425)

41. Pip and the Crow

Once upon a time the wind planted a small brown seed in a field.

'You belong to the One who makes things grow,' the wind said. 'Let the rain water you and the soil feed you, and one day your fruit will fill this field.'

A few weeks later the seed, who was called Pip, poked his head above ground only to see a big black crow hopping around the field planting seeds of its own. 'This field and all that is in it belongs to me,' cawed the crow.

A few more weeks passed. The crow's seeds poked their heads above ground, and the crow came back. This time it was pushing a wheelbarrow. 'Hello, everyone,' it cawed. 'I'm here to add sparkle to life.' Then it lifted a crate of lemonade out of the wheelbarrow.

Pip watched in amazement as it started watering its seeds with lemonade. 'This will put some colour in your leaves,' it cawed. And sure enough, no sooner did the tiny plants drink the lemonade, than they sprouted lots of bubbly orange leaves with purple spots.

'Oh, oh – our roots feel all fizzy,' they giggled.

Now deep in his roots Pip had a feeling that plants weren't meant to drink lemonade.

'No lemonade for me,' he told the crow firmly. 'I belong to the One who makes things grow. I only drink rain-water.'

'Haw . . . haw . . . haw!' the crow cawed nastily. 'Hear that, everyone? Pip only drinks rain-water. That's why he's so green.'

'Hee . . . hee . . . hee! We're glad we're orange with purple spots and not plain green like Pip,' laughed the plants.

It wasn't very nice to be laughed at, but Pip just got on with the business of growing. The rain watered him and the soil fed him and before long he was the biggest plant in the field.

A few weeks passed and the crow came back. 'Hello, everyone!' it cawed, as it pushed its wheelbarrow towards them. 'I'm here to make you all taller.' Then it took out a spade and a bag of gunpowder.

Pip watched in amazement as it began digging the gunpowder into the ground. 'This will speed up your growth,' it told its plants. And it did. No sooner had the orange plants got a taste of the gunpowder than they shot up high in the air.

'Look! We've turned into trees,' they cried.

Now deep in his roots Pip had the feeling that trees weren't meant to eat gunpowder.

'No gunpowder for me,' he told the crow firmly. 'I belong to the One who makes things grow. I get everything I need from the soil.'

'Haw . . . haw . . . haw!' the crow cawed nastily. 'Hear that, everyone? Pip gets everything he needs from the soil. That's why he's so small and weedy.'

'Hee . . . hee . . . hee! We're twice his size,' laughed the trees.

It wasn't very nice being looked down on, but Pip just got on with the business of growing. The rain watered him and the soil fed him. He grew and grew until eventually he was the tallest, strongest tree in the field. What's more, he had lots of good fruit on his branches, while the purple oranges on the crow's trees kept exploding.

When the crow saw the glossy apples ripening on Pip, its beady eyes gleamed with desire. It longed to have this fruit for itself. So it came up with a crafty scheme. Over the next few weeks it built a nest in each of the purple orange trees and laid three eggs in every nest. Before long the eggs had hatched into a flock of baby birds, all squawking hungrily.

Then the big black crow flew over to Pip. 'See, you are surrounded by a flock of hungry birds,' it told him. 'Any day now they will be big enough to attack your fruit and gobble it up. But I am willing to sit in your branches and protect you, if only you will say that your fruit belongs to me.'

'But it doesn't,' said Pip. 'My fruit belongs to the One who makes things grow.'

When the crow heard this, it was furious. 'Attack! Attack!' it cawed. And immediately the young birds rose from their nests and swooped towards Pip, beaks at the ready.

It wasn't very nice being threatened, but Pip knew who to call on in an emergency. 'Help me, wind,' he cried at the top of his voice. 'My fruit is about to be gobbled up by hungry crows!'

Immediately the wind rose up and came roaring and howling and raging across the field. It picked up the black crow and its offspring and the purple orange trees with their exploding fruit, and flung them into outer space. Pip was safe. The wind had come to his rescue. The only problem was it had blown all his apples to the ground.

'Oh dear!' sighed Pip. 'Everything's gone wrong.'

'No it hasn't,' laughed the wind. 'Scattering your fruit is part of the plan.'

So Pip got on with the business of growing. Time passed, and a wonderful thing happened. The seeds from his scattered fruit put down roots. The rain watered them. The soil fed them. They got taller and taller until Pip stood at the centre of a field full of apple trees. Then he praised the One who makes things grow.

And they all lived fruitfully ever after.

Teaching point

God is the One who makes things grow.

Bible reading

1 Corinthians 3:5–6.

Application

After telling the story hold up a card with part of 1 Corinthians 3:6 copied onto it: 'God . . . makes things grow.' Show the group pictures of one or two things that God makes grow and get them to shout out the names of other things that could be added to the list, e.g. flowers, vegetables, hair, toenails, animals, people. Then say that as well as making things grow in the outside world, God wants to make his own life grow in our hearts – something which happens when we belong to Christ. Finish by teaching the action rhyme below.

Action rhyme

From a tiny pip, small as a pea   (*hold pip between finger and thumb*)
God can grow a fruitful tree.   (*spreading gesture*)
From the seed of faith – a tiny start   (*plant seed in heart*)
The life of God grows in my heart.   (*repeat spreading gesture*)

Songs

All things bright and beautiful (JP 6)
Come, you thankful people, come (JP 32)
I'm feeding on the living bread (JP 104)
We plough the fields and scatter (JP 267)
Yes God is good – in earth and sky (JP 293)
At harvest time we celebrate (JP 311)
Have you got an appetite? (SOFK 52, JP 357)
It takes an almighty hand, to make your harvest grow (JP 395)
The Word of the Lord is planted in my heart (JP 473)
We need to grow, grow, grow, grow (JP 484)

NOVEMBER

All Creatures Great and Small

42. What a Job!

The first man, Adam, had plenty to do.
The garden he lived in was a bit like a zoo.
It was packed full of animals, insects and birds
Roaming around in flocks and herds.
Some were big, some were tiny, some were wild, some were
    tame.
But Adam had the job of giving each a name.
So he told all the creatures to get themselves in line
And then they came before him, one at a time.

At the front of the queue, making Adam's head sore
Was a large, hairy creature with a very loud roar.
'Quiet now!' said Adam. 'This is nothing but a try on.

You don't scare me. I'm calling you a LION.'
Next came a creature with a soft velvet nose.
It waved long ears as it nibbled Adam's toes.
'Oh p . . . lease,' said Adam. 'That's a very bad habit.
Off you go – and by the way – I'm calling you a RABBIT.'
The creature who came next had scales on its skin.
It crawled up to Adam and gave a toothy grin.
'Wow!' gasped Adam. 'You've a cracker of a smile.
I know,' he added. 'You can be a CRACODILE.'
After that came a pig, a cow, a cat, a donkey,
A butterfly, a snake, a mouse, a spider and a monkey.
And so time passed – easy-peasy – fun and games
Until, suddenly – disaster – Adam ran out of names.

He was looking at a creature with antlers tall as trees.
He scratched his head, he racked his brains, but it was as if
    his mind had seized.
He cried: 'Oh *dear*!' And the creature did a dance.
A DEER it was – it never knew its name was just by
    chance.
And still Adam's problem hadn't gone away.
There was an animal standing waiting and he'd no name to
    say.
The creature before him was very very big.
'Ummmm . . . would you like to be a crocofly?' he asked it.
    'Or a mousekey? Or a butterpig?'
The creature looked disgusted. It shook its floppy ears.
Oh help! thought Adam. This name could take me years.
And then he heard a soft voice speaking in his head:
'Adam!' whispered God. 'Try elephant instead.'
'ELEPHANT!' cried Adam. And off the creature went.
This was just the name it wanted. It was happy and
    content.
Adam grinned and looked up. 'Thank you, God,' he cried.
'I know I'll get the job done with you here at my side.'

And so he carried on with joy – the names came thick and
fast:
Squirrel, dog, gorilla – the whole parade went past.
'Well, that's that,' said Adam. 'Tea-time at last.'

'Pssst,' whispered God. 'Look towards the setting sun.
There is something in the distance – a creature still to
come.'
Adam looked and sure enough he saw a sort of lump.
'No need to wait for that,' he said. 'It's just a crawling
bump.'
'Bumps don't crawl,' God murmured, as Adam turned to go.
'That's still a living creature, even if it's rather slow.'
And Adam got the message. It was up to him to care.
How long the creature took to come was neither here nor
there.
The crawling bump came creeping on, slow but full of
purpose,
And Adam waited patiently to tell it, 'You're a
TORTOISE.'
And then he said to God: 'I'm glad I didn't go away.'
And God said: 'So am I, Adam. You've done good work
today.'

Teaching point

God gives us the job of caring for his world.

Bible readings

Genesis 1:26–31; Genesis 2:19.

Telling this story

Beforehand draw six simple illustrations of a lion, a rabbit, a crocodile, a deer, an elephant and a tortoise (or be prepared to mime them). With the lion, the rabbit, the crocodile and the tortoise, allow the children to guess the names of the animals before showing the illustrations. With the deer and the elephant, show them the picture and get them to tell you the name before Adam works it out.

Application

At the end of the story/poem hold up a card which says 'WELL DONE'. Point out that it's nice when people say 'well done' to us. It's nice when we do good work in school and the teacher says 'well done'. It's nice when we do good team-work in the playground or on the football pitch and friends say 'well done'. But the best thing of all is when God says 'well done'. Point out that in the imaginary story God said 'well done' to Adam because he had cared for the tortoise even though he was tired. God wants us all to care for his creation. Finish by praying that we will do that caring work well.

Songs

All things bright and beautiful (JP 6)
God who made the earth (JP 63)
Have you seen the pussycat sitting on the wall (SOFK 53, JP 72)
If I were a butterfly (SOFK 74, JP 94)
I have seen the golden sunshine (JP 99)
Think of a world without any flowers (JP 254)
Who put the colours in the rainbow (SOFK 191, JP 288)
God in His love lent us this planet (JP 347)
He made the water wet (JP 359)
Large creatures, small creatures (JP 415)
When we look up to the sky (JP 495)

43. In the Days of Noah

(Remembrance Sunday)

Tilly was a young ant – a very intelligent young ant who was determined to master the art of writing and spelling. She spent hours each day going over the alphabet, giving each letter its proper name and linking it with the sound it made. 'A makes the sound ah,' she would say. 'B makes the sound buh, C makes the sound cuh.' Then she would practise writing out simple rhymes in the dust – things like 'A for At', 'B for Bat' and 'C for Cat'.

One day, as Tilly was working away, the Queen ant came out of the anthill for a breath of fresh air.

'What are you doing?' she asked Tilly.

'Writing poetry,' Tilly said.

'Well I never!' the Queen said, looking impressed. 'I'm

very glad to discover a poet in my anthill – especially with Grandma and Grandpa Ant's five thousandth wedding anniversary coming up. How about writing a poem to celebrate it?'

'I'd love to,' said Tilly. And she meant it. Grandma and Grandpa were the oldest ants in the anthill and they were Tilly's favourite relatives. She called in on them regularly, although she always left the minute they started talking about the old days. Tilly had no interest in the days of Noah. She was far too involved in the here and now. Still, she knew she would have to bring the past into her anniversary poem.

'In honour of the occasion I shall write my poem in the language ants spoke before the great flood,' she told the Queen.

'Did ants speak a different language then?' asked the Queen in some surprise.

'Indeed they did,' Tilly assured her.

'I never got good marks for general knowledge at school,' the Queen sighed. 'However, I shall look forward to hearing your poem at the anniversary ball.'

Delighted with the Queen's request, Tilly got to work. First she thought up the words of her poem in the language of the present:

Dear Grandmother and Grandfather, all we want to say
Is that we hope that you will have a very happy day.
This poem is in the language you spoke when you were small
To bring back happy memories at your anniversary ball.

Then she translated it into the language of the past. And finally she got a helpful snail to trace the poem out on an oak leaf. 'A work for an important occasion like this needs to be in silver slime,' she explained. 'I want Granny and Grandpa to be able to frame it and hang it on their wall.'

The day of the anniversary ball arrived and, for the first time in hundreds of ant-years, work in the anthill stopped. The whole colony gathered together underground. There was music and dancing. The ants drank dew and feasted on cake crumbs. And then at the height of the proceedings Tilly stood up to read her anniversary poem, which had to be propped up by dozens of workers since the leaf was a great deal bigger than she was.

'Your Majesty, worker ants and guard ants,' she began. 'I dedicate this poem, written in the language ants spoke before the flood – to the oldest ants in this anthill, Grandfather and Grandmother Ant, to celebrate their wedding anniversary.'

Everyone clapped politely.

'Ahem.' Tilly cleared her throat.

'Dear Grinfither ind Grinmother, ill we wint to sigh
Is thit we hope thit you will hive i very hippy die.
This poem is in the lingwidge you spoke when you were smill
To bring bick hippy memories it this inniversiry bill.'

There was a puzzled silence when Tilly had finished reading her poem. She glanced round and realised that no one had understood it. Obviously they weren't tuned in to the language of the past. What really shocked her, though, was that by the look of things even the guests of honour hadn't appreciated her efforts. Grandmother and Grandfather seemed as puzzled as everyone else. In fact Grandmother Ant even looked a little upset. 'It's a very gloomy poem, Tilly,' she complained. 'Did you have to go on about sighs and bills and dying?'

'You don't understand, Granny,' cried Tilly. 'I had to change all the letter "a"s to "i"s because there *were* no "a"s in those days. So sigh means say, and die means day, and bill means ball.'

At this Grandmother and Grandfather looked more puzzled than ever. 'Whatever makes you think there were no "a"s in those days?' Grandfather frowned.

'Because you told me so. You told me they were the days of no "ah",' Tilly cried.

Immediately Grandmother and Grandfather burst out laughing. 'If you'd only listened to us a bit more you'd understand that the days of Noah have nothing to do with the letters of the alphabet,' they laughed. 'Noah wasn't a missing letter, he was a man.'

Oh dear! Suddenly Tilly realised how little she'd understood.

'Never mind,' said the Queen. 'Now you know the "ah"s weren't missing, you can take the bills and dying out of your poem and make it more cheerful.'

And with that the musician ants struck up again and everyone got on with the ball.

Later, though, when life was back to normal, Tilly paid her grandparents a special visit. 'I want you to tell me all about the days of Noah,' she said.

So Grandmother and Grandfather told her all about the wickedness, and about the ark and about God sending the flood to destroy human life so there could be a fresh start, and about the man, Noah, saving two of every animal, insect and bird.

'You mean if it hadn't been for what Noah did, we would have all been wiped out?' Tilly gasped.

Grandmother and Grandfather nodded.

'Imagine! I owe my life to someone and I never even knew it,' Tilly marvelled. 'How come you didn't tell me this sooner?'

'How come you didn't ask us, Tilly?' her grandparents smiled.

Teaching point

The importance of sharing memories – especially of things God has done.

Bible reading

Psalm 44:1–3.

Telling the story

In order to tell the story effectively, have copies of Tilly's poem to show the group: one written correctly, and a second with the 'a's changed to 'i's.

Application

After telling the story hold up a poppy and ask the group what poppies help us to remember (those who gave up their lives in the war). Remind the group how, in the story, Tilly discovered she owed her life to someone she'd never met. Who was it? (Noah.) In the same way we may never know how much we owe to those who died in the war. But we can begin to find out how much we and the people around us owe to God. Finish by encouraging the group to ask older Christians to share their memories – especially memories of things God has done.

Songs

I sing a song of the saints of God (JP 115)
Mister Noah built an ark (JP 167)
Oh the Lord looked down from His window in the sky
  (JP 184)
Sing we the King who is coming to reign (JP 218)

We've a story to tell to the nations (JP 272)
God in His love for us lent us this planet (JP 347)
Hey! Hey! Anybody listening? (JP 362)
Noah was the only good man (JP 432)
Old man Noah built an ark (JP 440)

44. Under God

(A true story from the life of Abraham Lincoln)

As a boy Abe lived in a log cabin. He hardly ever went to school. Instead, he spent most of his time out of doors, chopping down trees and working on the farm. He grew enormously tall and enormously strong. Still there were some things about the outdoor life he never took to – fishing, for example, and hunting. Despite his great strength, young Abe had a very soft heart and he hated to see any living creature breathe its last.

When he was twenty-two Abe gave up farming and went to work in a town called New Salem. By this time he was a black-haired, grey-eyed giant of a man (six foot four inches tall) and his arrival created a bit of a stir, especially among the local gang who terrorised the streets. They were known as the Clary Grove Brothers. And their leader, Jack Armstrong, prided himself on being the toughest guy about town. Abe didn't like fighting any more than he liked hunting, but he realised he would get no peace until he'd fought Jack Armstrong, so eventually he agreed to a wrestling match.

On the day of the match the Clary gang were out in force to support their leader. 'Come on, Jack. Flatten the guy,' they cheered. But next thing, they saw their hero being lifted right off his feet by his opponent, who held him, legs dangling, at arm's length.

After this show of strength Abe had no more trouble with the Clary Grove Brothers. In fact he and Jack became good friends. Soon the whole gang were behaving better and, thanks to Abe's influence, New Salem had become a much safer place.

Time passed and Abraham began to influence how the country was run. He made a name for himself travelling around speaking to huge crowds, but he lost none of his soft-heartedness. Once, while making a journey on horseback, he found two little birds that had tumbled out of their nest. Instead of riding on, he kept all his companions waiting while he searched for the nest so that he could put the birds back in again. 'If I had not put those birds back in their nest where the mother would feed them, I would not have slept all night,' he said.

Then one November Abraham Lincoln was elected President of the United States. It is hard to imagine a man who could have lost sleep over the death of a sparrow sending soldiers into battle. But, as President, that was what Lincoln had to do. The years of his presidency were one of the worst periods in the history of the American people – a period when the country passed through a terrible civil war.

At the beginning of the war, although he had a great respect for the Bible, Abraham Lincoln would not have described himself as a Christian. He was a good man, an honest man, a man who cared for all God's creatures. But he didn't know their Creator in a personal way.

Then came the turning point. It was another grey November day and the President had been asked to speak at a cemetery (or graveyard) where thousands of soldiers were buried. Looking at the rows and rows of graves, Lincoln's soft heart was moved with sadness at the thought of so many lives lost. He longed for a new age of freedom and forgiveness. Yet he knew human power couldn't bring that about. Then, suddenly, it struck him. Only God could make the future better than the past. And there and then, looking out over those rows of crosses, Abraham Lincoln committed his life to Christ.

As a result he added two very important words to his speech that day. He encouraged his listeners to build a better future. And he encouraged them to do it *under God*.

Under God. Those were the two small words that said so much; two words Abraham Lincoln used to tell the world an all-powerful caring Creator was in control.

Teaching point

God, the all-powerful Creator, is in control of his world.

Bible readings

Matthew 10:28–31; Deuteronomy 33:27.

Application

After telling the story, lay a narrow strip of paper across the floor and ask the group to imagine it is a narrow ledge between two cliffs with a raging torrent underneath. How would they feel about walking across it? Then ask what difference it would make if they knew there was a safety-net underneath, so that if they overbalanced and fell the net would catch them. Point out that in the story Abraham Lincoln discovered that God was his safety-net. Then introduce the Bible verses as two short readings which remind us of God's overall care and control.

Songs

Be bold, be strong, for the Lord your God is with you
  (SOFK 6, JP 14)
Father, hear the prayer we offer (JP 41)
He's got the whole wide world in His hands (JP 78)
My God is so big, so strong and so mighty (SOFK 134,
  JP 169)
My Lord is higher than a mountain (JP 170)
There are hundreds of sparrows, thousands, millions
  (JP 246)
For the foolishness of God is wiser than men's wisdom
  (JP 340)
God whose love is everywhere (JP 353)
Think big: an elephant (JP 479)

45. Lost and Found

(Based on a true story)

Andy was a man who wanted a dog, and Poppy was a dog who wanted an owner. They met at the dogs' home and it was love at first sight.

'This is the dog for me,' Andy said the moment he saw the medium-sized brown collie with a bit of Alsatian thrown in. He wasn't even put off by her barking.

'Calm down. It's all right,' he said as he crouched beside Poppy. She stopped barking at once, as if she knew instinctively that she could trust him.

For the next twelve months Andy and Poppy were rarely apart. They explored the countryside together and relaxed together in front of the TV. Andy even took Poppy away with him on business. Some dogs might not have enjoyed riding

248

in the car, but Poppy adored it. She would leap in the moment Andy opened the door, and as they drove along, she would sit with her nose against the passenger window, sniffing the scents that came in from outside.

Then one night, as Andy and Poppy travelled home, something terrible happened. The car went out of control, careering across the road and smashing into a wall. The crash sent Andy and Poppy flying out onto the road. Poppy was back on her feet immediately, but Andy didn't move. The dog stood beside him and licked his face, but he didn't open his eyes.

A few minutes passed, and suddenly the quiet of the night was shattered by the shriek of a siren. Terrified by the noise and the flashing blue lights Poppy bounded off into the shadows. There she watched two men in uniform wrap Andy in blankets and lift him into an ambulance. Next thing she saw was him being taken away. Desperate to be with him, she jumped up and gave chase; but the ambulance moved so fast, it left her behind. She returned to the car, only to find that it was being taken away too.

Poppy was alone on a main road and far from home. To begin with she dashed frantically to and fro, so that it was a miracle she wasn't run over. Then, towards morning, a driver rolled down his car window and yelled at her, and she raced off into the surrounding fields.

Meanwhile, in a hospital bed twenty miles away, Andy woke up with the worst headache he'd ever had in his life. 'A fractured skull' was what the doctors called it.

'What's going on? Where am I?' he groaned.

'You had a car accident,' a nurse told him.

For a moment Andy was silent, struggling to remember what had happened. When he did remember, the memory was even worse than the pain in his head. 'Poppy!' he cried. 'Where's Poppy?'

Everyone did their best to calm him down. 'Don't worry about your dog,' they said. 'We'll find her.'

Before long half the neighbourhood was on the look-out for a medium-sized brown collie with a bit of Alsatian thrown in. People were marvellous – strangers as well as friends. Local farmers left food outside to tempt the dog into their yards, and friends tramped through fields near the main road calling her name. But nothing came of it.

'Have you found her?' Andy would ask anxiously every time anyone came to visit, and the answer was always the same: 'No. Not yet.'

When Poppy had been missing for over a week, Andy took matters into his own hands. He got dressed and signed himself out of hospital. The doctors weren't happy, but nothing they could say would stop him. Fractured skull or no fractured skull, he was off to search for his pet.

Poppy, by this stage, had grown weak and thin. She had found herself a hiding-place, deep in a hedge behind a house, behind a garden shed. She didn't come out much – just for a few hours each night to scavenge round the rubbish bins. Sometimes she would find crusts of bread, and once she found a packet of ham which had passed its sell-by date. It wasn't enough to keep a medium-sized collie alive, but Poppy didn't care. Now that her master had gone, she didn't see much point in living.

The morning after Andy left hospital she was curled up as usual in her hiding-place, vaguely aware of all the usual morning sounds.

She heard the voices of the cattle in the nearby fields.

She heard the voices of birds singing in the hedgerow.

She heard the voices of children, leaving for school.

And then she heard a woman's voice call sharply from the upstairs window of the house: 'Who are you? What do you want?'

And she heard a man's voice answer: 'I'm here looking for my dog. She's a medium-sized brown collie with a bit of Alsatian thrown in.'

Two sentences. That was all it took to bring the animal exploding out of the hedge. And there he was, her master – pale and with a bandage round his head – but with his arms wide open and his face full of joy.

'Poppy!' Andy cried.

And she flung herself at him.

Her lonely days were over. The lost dog was found.

Teaching point

The joy of reunion with God.

Bible reading

Luke 15:1–7.

Application

After telling the story hold up a large blank face. Ask for a volunteer to come and draw an expression that shows how Andy felt when Poppy came out of the hedge. Hold up the smiling face and agree that Andy was overjoyed when he found Poppy. Then say that the Bible tells us that God is overjoyed when he is reunited with us. Point out that it was a car accident that separated Poppy from Andy. What is it that separates us from God? (Our sinful nature.) Read Luke 15:1–7. Finish by reminding the group that the moment Poppy heard Andy's voice she shot out of the hedge. Today, through Jesus, God is calling to us. Have we experienced the joy of being reunited with him?

Songs

Come let us sing of a wonderful love (JP 29)
Come on, let's get up and go (SOFK 16, JP 31)

'Follow Me' says Jesus (JP 46)
If you want joy, real joy, wonderful joy (JP 96)
In my need Jesus found me (JP 109)
I was lost but Jesus found me (JP 125)
I will sing the wondrous story (JP 127)
The Lord's my shepherd (SOFK 162)
I look out through the doorway (JP 371)
Wandering like lost sheep we were going our own way
　(JP 482)

DECEMBER

Giving and Receiving

46. Baby in Waiting

(Advent)

There is an old folk-tale in which the Wise Men, on their way
to Bethlehem, spend the night with a peasant girl called
Babushka. Before leaving, they ask her if she would like to
come with them to see the Christ-child. 'I can't,' she says.
'I'm too busy.' But once they've gone she changes her mind.
She packs up some gifts for the new-born King and sets off
for Bethlehem – only to find an empty stable. She's too late.
Mary, Joseph and the baby have moved on to Egypt.

OK, so that's the folk-tale. Now let's imagine that a class of
primary school children are putting this story on as a nativ-
ity play. It's the day of the dress rehearsal and one of them –
a boy called Matthew – is being teased by the Wise Men.

The Wise Men are his three chums, Raju, Jason and Keith,

and they're teasing Matthew because Matthew has the part of Joseph.

'Hey Matthew, what's it like to be married?' asks Jason.

'Matthew, your wife needs you,' calls Raju.

'She wants to hold your hand,' says Keith.

Now this is pretty annoying, but all Matthew really needs to do is point out that as Joseph he has the Wise Men kneeling at his feet. Instead he explodes like a box of fireworks. 'I hate girls, and I hate you too,' he yells. 'I'm never going to play with you again.'

The next day is the day of the performance. By ten o'clock the assembly hall is full of parents, and Miss Black, the children's teacher, is reminding Matthew of what he has to do.

'Remember, you come on in scene two,' she tells him. 'You stand behind the manger beside Mary. You wait until the Wise Men bring their gifts, then you take Mary's hand and lead her and baby Jesus off to Egypt.'

Matthew scowls. He *still* doesn't want to be Joseph, and he still hates the three Wise Men.

The play gets underway. Scene one, where the Wise Men stay overnight with Babushka, passes off smoothly.

Then comes scene two. Grimly Matthew trudges on stage with Mary and stands at her side. The Wise Men kneel before the manger and he snatches their gifts. As they get up, he lets his mind wander . . . until suddenly Mary (who is really called Megan) nudges him. '*Move*,' she mouths. Ooops! He wakes up to the fact that they should have left for Egypt five seconds ago and Miss Black is hissing, 'Hurry up!' from the wings.

No sooner do they reach the wings than there's a bit of a fuss. 'Oh no!' gasps Megan and tries to dash back on stage.

'You can't go back,' Miss Black stops her. 'The whole audience would notice.' Matthew frowns. Notice *what*? A quick glance over his shoulder, and he has his answer. Disaster! They've forgotten baby Jesus.

Scene three is the scene where Babushka is supposed to reach Bethlehem too late to see the Christ-child. The trouble is, thanks to Matthew and Megan, she isn't too late. Baby Jesus is still there – plain as punch – lying in the manger. And Matthew can see the parents in the first few rows all trying not to laugh.

Right in the middle of the very front row sits the vicar.

He says the closing prayer; then comes backstage, where Megan is sniffing into a tissue.

'I'd have remembered Jesus if I hadn't had to look after Matthew,' she sniffs.

You can imagine Matthew's feelings. He's heading for another explosion – ready to blow up at the first hint of teasing. Fortunately, though, the vicar has more sense.

'But I *loved* the way you left the doll in the manger,' he tells Megan. 'Your Christ-child, waiting for Babushka, reminded me that God is very patient and waits for us too.'

These words make everyone feel better. Megan cheers up and Matthew calms down. He likes the sound of this God – a God who gives second chances, who isn't rushing to say, 'Too late!' And then another thought strikes him. There's something this patient God is waiting for him to do.

Can you guess what it is?

Drrring goes the bell. It's lunch-time.

Megan skips off all smiles because forgetting baby Jesus has been so clever. And Matthew shoots into the playground to put things right with the Wise Men.

Teaching point

God is patient.

Bible reading

2 Peter 3:8–9.

Application

After the story hold up a blank sheet of paper and say that you are going to write on it the most disappointing words in the English language. Write up the words 'TOO LATE'. Remind the group that in the story Matthew discovered these are two words God doesn't want to say. Then show the group a picture of baby Jesus with the second half of 2 Peter 3:9 copied underneath. Say that just as God kept his promise and sent Jesus into the world as a baby, so one day he has promised that Jesus will return to the world as King. In the meantime, he waits patiently for people to turn to him. Finish by thanking God for his patience and praying that we may respond to his love.

Songs

As with gladness men of old (JP 9)
I have decided to follow Jesus (SOFK 79, JP 98)
In our work and in our play (JP 108)
The Virgin Mary had a baby boy (JP 251)
The wise may bring their learning (JP 253)
We three kings of Orient are (JP 271)
I've come to a time when I must change (JP 383)

47. Out of the Cupboard

(A true story for Bible Sunday)

One morning the pupils at Chefoo school in Malaysia had a special visitor at assembly. His name was Nathan, and he was a Chinese Christian from the nearby village. He'd come that morning to tell the children about a group of people living deep in the jungle that surrounded their school – the Orang Asli people, they were called.

'The Orang Asli were the very first people to live in this part of the world,' Nathan explained. 'They build their homes on platforms high off the ground, and they hunt for food, using poisoned darts and long blow pipes.'

He went on to say that because they lived in villages deep in the jungle, most of these people had never had the chance to hear about Jesus. 'For a long time I've been wanting to share the good news with them,' he finished. 'Please pray that God will show me how to go about it.'

In the weeks that followed the Chefoo pupils prayed a great deal for Uncle Nathan and the Orang Asli people. Then one afternoon some eight- and nine-year-olds were tidying a cupboard in their classroom when they happened to come across a Bible written in the Malay language. It had been left at the school by a missionary couple, and the children knew that if they put it back in the cupboard it could sit there for years.

Suddenly one of them had a bright idea. 'I know. Let's give this Bible to Uncle Nathan,' she said.

So the pupils got in touch with Nathan, who called back at the school and picked the Bible up.

The next week Nathan packed this Bible and some sweets into a cloth bag and set off into the jungle on his motor-bike. He was on his way to an Orang Asli village. For several hours the bike bumped and spluttered along the steeply winding track until finally a cluster of thatched huts all standing on stilts came into view. Nathan had reached his destination. Praying that God would show him who to talk to and what to say, he stopped his bike and waited for some Orang Aslis to come along.

First to appear on the scene were a group of inquisitive children. Nathan was relieved to see they didn't have blow pipes! 'Hello,' he said. 'I've got some sweets here. Would you like to taste them?'

The children smiled as Nathan passed the sweets round. Then he asked if they would take him to speak to their mums and dads.

Tugging at his jacket, the children led the way to the biggest house in the village – the one where the head man lived. Next thing Nathan knew he was standing in a bamboo room, high off the ground, facing a crowd of villagers.

Out came the Malay Bible, and for the next half an hour

the Chinese Christian talked to these Orang Asli people about Jesus.

When he finally shut the book, there was a moment of silence.

Then the head man spoke on behalf of the group. 'What you have told us is good,' he announced. 'We want to become followers of Jesus.'

Nathan blinked, amazed that things had happened so fast. Carefully he explained what following Jesus meant and said it was something every person should decide for themselves. Then he asked anyone who wanted to follow Jesus to put up their hand. Immediately all twenty-three adults and most of the children waved their arms in the air.

As the head man lowered his hand he pointed to the Malay Bible. 'Now we are Christians,' he said, 'we need a book like yours to teach us more.'

So Nathan left the Bible in the village. The people started reading it and before long there were so many growing Christians in that jungle village that they appointed a pastor and built their own bamboo church on stilts like their homes.

All in all it was a real answer to prayer.

And needless to say the Chefoo pupils were thrilled when they heard how wonderfully God had used their Bible. At the same time they weren't surprised really. For they'd known all along that it was a book with the power to change lives – which is why they hadn't left it in the cupboard.

Teaching point

The Bible is a book that changes lives.

Bible reading

2 Timothy 3:16.

Application

After telling the story hold up the words of 2 Timothy 3:16 and get the group to read them aloud. Then say that although there is lots to think about in this verse, its meaning can be summed up very simply: *the Bible is a book that changes lives*. Remind the group how the Bible in the story had to be taken out of the cupboard before lives could be changed. Finish by pointing out that the Bible can't change our lives unless we are taking it out and reading it too.

Songs

Make the Book live to me, O Lord (JP 163)
The best book to read is the Bible (JP 234)
Father, Your Word (JP 338)
Have you got an appetite? (SOFK 52, JP 357)
I'm going to hide God's Word (JP 378)
I'm going to say my prayers (SOFK 87, JP 379)
I'm going to set my heart (JP 382)
If your empty tum is rumbling (JP 390)
The Word of God is living and active (JP 474)

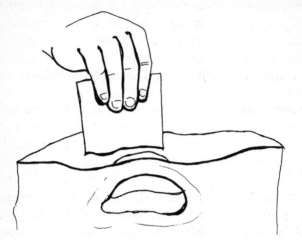

48. Message of Hope

(For Advent – based on a true story from Sri Lanka)

It was early December on the tropical island of Sri Lanka, and already the Rajasingham family were thinking about Christmas. Mr Rajasingham, who sang in the church choir, had started practising carols. Mrs Rajasingham had bought fresh spices for the special chicken curry the family would eat on Christmas Day. And the children, Ashok and Rani, were dropping hints – saying things like: 'I could really do with a new pair of trainers,' and, 'I'd love it if someone gave me a new skirt.'

Then came reports that 200 miles away, in the north of the island, fierce fighting had broken out. Sadly news of bombs and gun-attacks was not unusual, for beautiful Sri Lanka was a country torn by civil war. This time, though, the trouble in the north had become so bad that thousands of families had had to flee from their homes.

In Ashok and Rani's church the following Sunday their pastor told the congregation that many homeless people were now sheltering in school buildings, churches and temples. 'It's really hard for them,' he went on. 'They've very little food or medicine and scarcely any clean water to drink.'

During the service everyone prayed about the situation. Afterwards, though, some folk felt that God might be wanting them to do more than pray. 'It doesn't seem right that we should just carry on with all our usual Christmas celebrations when our brothers and sisters are starving,' Rani overheard someone say. 'After all, Christmas is about giving. We need to ask what Jesus would do if he were here.'

A few days later Mr Rajasingham came home from choir practice with important information. 'I heard this evening that a relief fund has been set up,' he told the family. 'The plan is to send trucks full of food and supplies to the north. But first we need to raise £1,000.'

A thousand pounds! Ashok and Rani gasped. In Sri Lanka a thousand pounds was a lot of money.

Next morning the children had something to say to their parents.

'You know the trainers I said I wanted for Christmas,' Ashok began. 'Well . . . I've been thinking. I'd rather you didn't buy me them. Give the money to the relief fund instead.'

Rani nodded. 'And please, I want you to give the money for my skirt too.'

To the fund organisers' delight lots of other church members were saying the same sort of things. Instead of spending money on themselves that Christmas, they wanted to give it to the relief fund. As a result, the target had been reached sooner than anyone expected. This was the good news. The bad news was a shock announcement that roads into the war-torn areas were only going to be open for three more days. In other words, if the church wanted to send food and supplies to the north, everything would have to be bought, packed up and loaded onto the trucks straight away.

Manpower – that was what was needed now. And once again the Rajasinghams didn't wait to be asked twice. As soon as they heard volunteers were needed they hurried down to the church hall. There they were each given a plastic bag and a list of what to put in it.

Eagerly Ashok and Rani got to work, ticking things off as they went: rice, sugar, candles, matches, powdered milk. Before long they'd reached the final item – a Christmas message.

The pastor had already explained what this meant.

'Before we seal each bag we're supposed to put in a message for the person who opens it,' Ashok said.

'It's hard to know what to write,' Rani said, picking up a little card and frowning. 'What sort of a message would you like to get if you were stuck in a school classroom over Christmas?'

Ashok looked thoughtful. 'I think I'd like to be reminded that God was there with me.'

Immediately Rani lifted her pen. She wrote two words on the card and then showed them to her brother. Remember Emmanuel,' they said.

'That's another name for Jesus,' the girl explained. 'It means "God with us".'

'Hey! I like that,' Ashok said, picking up a second card. 'I'm going to put "Remember Emmanuel" in my bag too.'

So the children worked on, message after message, bag after bag. The hours ticked past. It grew dark outside and then it began to get light again. And finally the last packages were sealed and loaded onto the waiting trucks.

'Hurrah!' everyone cheered as the engines started up and the vehicles roared off down the road.

Ashok turned to Rani. 'You know what,' he said. 'We haven't done any of the things we usually do, but this has been my best Christmas ever.'

'Mine too,' Rani agreed.

They said good-bye to their friends and joined their parents.

Then, tired but full of Christmas joy, the Rajasingham family returned home.

Teaching point

At Christmas we celebrate God coming to be with us on earth.

Bible reading

Matthew 1:18–23.

Application

After telling the story hold up the words which Rani wrote on her card: 'Remember Emmanuel'. Check that the group remember what Emmanuel means. Point out that sometimes in the middle of all our Christmas celebrations we can forget what we're meant to be celebrating – the fact that Almighty God loved us so much that he was ready to leave the glory of heaven and live with us on earth. Then say that we are more likely to remember the true meaning when, like the Christians in the story, we concentrate more on giving than on getting. Finish by teaching the chorus below.

Chorus *(may be sung to 'Plaisir d'Amour')*

At Christmas-time
We have a lot of fun
But most of all we remember
God sent his Son.

Our homes are bright
The rooms inside are warm
But in a cattle-shed bare
Jesus Christ was born.

He came to earth
Out of love for you and me
That's the best Christmas present
There'll ever be.

Songs

Away in a manger, no crib for a bed (JP 12)
Infant holy (JP 110)
Jesus, Name above all names (SOFK 110, JP 141)
O come, O come, Emmanuel (JP 177)
The Virgin Mary had a baby boy (JP 251)
A special star is in the sky (JP 305)
Born in the night (JP 313)
Christmas is a time (JP 321)
Come and join the celebration (JP 323)
Crackers and turkeys and pudding and cream (JP 327)
Sing and celebrate (JP 456)
This Child, secretly comes in the night (JP 480)
From heaven You came (SOFK 31, JP 341)

49. *Happy Christmas*

(Christmas Day)

On Christmas Day, Lowly the glow-worm crawled out from under a stone straight into the path of an oncoming thrush.

For most worms this would have been a disaster, but Lowly was glad. He'd just had a big disappointment. He'd found out that morning that worms don't grow into snakes and beetles don't grow into birds, and now he reckoned that being eaten was the only way he'd become part of anything bigger.

'Hello, Thrush,' he said. 'I'm your Christmas dinner.'

But instead of gobbling Lowly up, the thrush turned aside, brushing away a tear with its wing. 'Don't talk to me about Christmas,' it sighed. 'All my chicks have left the nest. I've nothing to celebrate.'

267

'I've nothing to celebrate either,' the voice of a pine tree murmured sorrowfully above their heads. 'This time last year I was a Christmas tree, surrounded by presents and covered with decorations. And now look at me: stripped bare and dumped in the garden.'

'Well there you are then,' shrugged Lowly. 'We're all in the same boat – or rather the same garden. So I suppose we might as well *not* celebrate Christmas together.'

The thrush and the pine tree agreed this seemed the sensible thing to do.

Then, just as they had gathered together in a gloomy huddle, they saw a small boy wandering along the path towards them, crying bitterly.

His sobs tore at the thrush's soft heart and she immediately asked what was wrong.

'It's my birthday,' cried the child. 'But my family don't care. My brothers and sisters won't even talk to me. They say they don't have time.'

'What a shame!' said the thrush. 'But it doesn't mean they don't love you. They're just taken up with Christmas, that's all.'

Her words were meant to comfort the child, but they seemed to make him more unhappy than ever. He cried so hard that the glow-worm, the thrush and the tree put their heads together and came up with an idea.

'Child, we weren't planning to do anything this year,' they said. 'But if you like we'll have a special celebration for your birthday.'

The child stopped crying. 'Oh yes! I'd like that very much.'

So the glow-worm, the thrush and the tree set about cheering the child up. Lowly went first. 'Watch this! I'm an acrobat,' he told the child. Then he crawled all the way to the very tip of the pine tree, where he stood on his head and pointed his tail-light to the moon. 'Look, I'm shining just for you. Happy Birthday, Child,' he called.

After that the thrush gave a concert. She opened her beak and sang a dozen lovely songs, finishing with the special lullaby she had sung to her chicks. 'Listen, I'm singing just for you. Happy Birthday, Child,' she trilled.

Finally the tree made a presentation. 'Child, I have gifts to give you,' it said. 'Hold out your hands.'

So the child stood under the tree and cupped his hands, and the tree filled them with sweet-smelling pine cones.

'See, I'm giving all that I have to you. Happy Birthday, Child,' it called.

The child clapped with delight. 'Glow-worm, you shine like a star. Thrush, you sing like an angel. Tree, your gifts are as precious as gold,' he cried. 'It's been a wonderful birthday.'

As he spoke, the joy on his face seemed to light up the garden. And his companions realised something. Celebrating the child's birthday had helped them forget their own sorrows and disappointments.

'Dear Child,' said Lowly. 'You've made today very special.'

'Yes,' agreed the thrush. 'You've helped us get over our troubles – just as we hope we've helped you get over yours.'

The child smiled, but he shook his head. 'I don't have my own troubles,' he said.

'But you told us about them,' cried Lowly. 'You were miserable. You said your brothers and sisters didn't care about your birthday.'

Again the child shook his head. 'No, no. You don't understand. I wasn't crying for myself. I was crying for them. I was crying because people miss the whole meaning of Christmas when they leave me out.'

At these words the thrush's heart leapt, the tree started to tremble and Lowly almost tumbled to the ground.

'Child, who are you? What is your name?' they cried.

There was a flash of understanding – of incredible brightness – and the child had gone. It could have been a dream, but the three friends knew better.

'He was here,' the tree rustled.

'In our garden,' sang the thrush.

'Meeting with us,' glowed Lowly. 'Turning our darkness to light.'

Teaching point

Putting Christ into Christmas.

Bible reading

John 1:1–14.

Application

After telling the story hold up the words 'Happy Birthday' and ask if anyone has a birthday in December. Point out that sometimes people with birthdays in December feel hard done by, because in the fun and excitement of Christmas their birthdays get overlooked. Then say that in the story we heard about another birthday that is often overlooked – the birth of Christ. Hold up the words 'Happy Christmas' and point out that the letters C-H-R-I-S-T are right in the middle of the message. They remind us that we're meant to be celebrating Christ's birthday, and that the way to a truly happy Christmas is through meeting with him.

Songs

Infant holy (JP 110)

Mary had a little baby, Mary had a little baby (JP 164)

A special star is in the sky (JP 305)

Born in the night (JP 313)

Christmas is a time (JP 321)

Christmas isn't Christmas till it happens in your heart (JP 322)

Come and join the celebration (JP 323)
Crackers and turkeys and pudding and cream (JP 327)
Girls and boys, leave your toys, make no noise (JP 344)
From heaven You came (SOFK 31, JP 341)

50. Little Sister

Across the land church bells rang out. A baby prince had been born. Elder Brother heard the sound at his carpenter's bench, and immediately began to carve a gift for the child. Younger Brother heard the sound at his anvil and immediately began making a gift too. Little Sister heard the bells on her swing in the garden and she swung up joyfully higher and higher, up and down in time to their peals.

That evening Elder Brother came home with a fine cricket bat and Younger Brother came home with a pair of soft leather boots.

'We will take our gifts to the palace tomorrow,' they said.

'I wish I had something for the baby prince,' Little Sister sighed.

Next morning, when the brothers came down for break-fast, Little Sister was dressed to go out. 'I'm coming to the palace with you,' she told them.

'Don't be silly,' said Elder Brother. 'You've nothing to bring.'

'Yes I have,' Little Sister said, taking a box from under her cloak. She opened the box and the brothers saw that it was full of pages covered in her wobbly handwriting. 'I've written a story,' she told them. 'I stayed up all last night finishing it so I could give it to the baby prince today.'

The brothers got into a huddle. 'We can't let her give her silly story to the prince,' whispered Younger Brother. 'It would be embarrassing.'

'Don't worry. Let her come with us,' Elder Brother whispered back. 'I have a cunning plan.'

So the two brothers and Little Sister set off for the palace – Elder Brother with his cricket bat, Younger Brother with his boots and Little Sister with her story in the box. After they'd walked for a couple of hours, Elder Brother suggested that they should stop for a rest.

'Sit down, Little Sister and we'll light a fire,' he said.

'All right,' said Little Sister, very glad to sit down by the fire, for it was the middle of winter and she was cold.

Then Elder Brother said, 'Lie down, Little Sister and we'll take a nap.'

'All right,' said Little Sister, very glad to lie down, for she'd been walking all morning and she was tired.

They all lay down by the fire and before long Little Sister was sound asleep.

The minute she fell asleep Elder Brother jumped up. 'Quickly,' he said. 'There's no time to lose.' He snatched Little Sister's box, took out the story and tossed the pages into the fire.

'That takes care of that,' he said. 'Now – on with our gifts to the palace! We'll tell Little Sister we took her story too.'

'Good thinking,' Younger Brother said as he strode off down the path. 'With any luck she won't wake up until we're back.'

But Little Sister didn't sleep until the brothers got back. Instead she woke up a few moments after they had left. And the first thing she saw was the empty box.

'My story! What's happened to my story?' she cried.

'Your brothers burned it,' twittered a blue tit. 'I saw them open the box and throw the pages in the fire.'

When Little Sister heard that her story had been burned, she sat quite still, singing to herself, until the fire went out. Then she scooped the ashes of her story up into the box and continued on her way.

A few hours later she arrived at the palace. 'Through here, Miss,' said a guard, and she was shown into a waiting-room. Looking round, she saw that it was full of everything a child could possibly need. In one corner was a pile of cricket bats and in another a row of tiny boots. 'Through here, Miss,' the guard said again, and Little Sister followed him on into the Great Hall where the Queen sat on a silver throne between red velvet curtains, with the baby prince in a golden cradle by her side.

Little Sister was just in time to see her brothers present their gifts.

First Elder Brother went forward with his cricket bat.

'Thank you,' the Queen said, handing it to a servant. 'I wish my son had a hundred arms, for then he would be able to play with all the bats he's been given.'

Next, Younger Brother presented his boots.

'Thank you,' said the Queen handing them to another servant. 'I wish my son had 200 legs, for then he would be able to wear all the boots he's received.'

By this stage Little Sister had reached the throne.

'Your Majesty, I've something in this box that no one else has given your son,' she said.

The Queen looked interested. 'Well . . . what is it?'

'It started out as a beautiful story,' said Little Sister. 'But my brothers burned the pages in the fire.'

The Queen looked puzzled. 'So what's in the box then?'

'A surprise,' smiled Little Sister. 'You'll have to open it and see.'

The Queen took the box and lifted the lid. Immediately a beautiful perfume filled the hall. Everyone smelled it – the scent of moonlight and laughter and spring showers and birdsong.

'Why! It's the memory of your story!' breathed the Queen. 'What a wonderful gift!'

Then she took Little Sister's hand and led her over to the cradle.

And Little Sister placed the box at the baby's feet.

Teaching point

Letting the memory of the Christmas story strike us afresh this year.

Bible reading

Luke 2:1–14.

Application

Use a box (with a Bible concealed inside) as a visual aid while telling the story. After telling it remind the group how, in the story, the box held something beautiful and surprising. Then say that your box holds a surprise for us now. Take out the Bible. Read Luke 2:1–14 and ask the group what they have just heard (the story of Christ's birth). This is the story we remember each Christmas. This Christmas, as we remember it, may the wonder of its message strike us afresh.

Songs

God so loved the world He sent to us Jesus (JP 59)
Infant holy (JP 110)
Mary had a little baby, Mary had a little baby (JP 164)
See Him lying on a bed of straw (JP 214)
The Virgin Mary had a baby boy (JP 251)
Christmas isn't Christmas till it happens in your heart
  (JP 322)
Crackers and turkeys and pudding and cream (JP 327)
It was on a starry night (JP 396)
The shepherds found the stable (JP 471)
This Child, secretly comes in the night (JP 480)
From heaven You came (SOFK 31, JP 341)

Subject Index

Scripture Index

50 Five-Minute Stories

by Lynda Neilands

'Please tell us a story…'

When you want something to fill the next five or ten minutes, something that will hold the children's attention and stay in their minds, this book will provide the fresh ideas and once-upon-a-time stories you need.

LYNDA NEILANDS is the author of the Brownie Guide Handbook as well as several children's novels. She lives in Belfast with her husband and twin sons – who have road-tested these stories.